justinguitar.com
Vintage Songbook

Published by
Wise Publications
14-15 Berners Street, London W1T 3LJ, UK.

Exclusive Distributors:
Music Sales Limited
Distribution Centre, Newmarket Road,
Bury St Edmunds, Suffolk IP33 3YB, UK.
Music Sales Corporation
180 Madison Avenue, 24th Floor, New York NY 10016, USA.
Music Sales Pty Limited
Units 3-4, 17 Willfox Street, Condell Park NSW 2200, Australia.

Order No. AM1005169
ISBN: 978-1-78038-686-7
This book © Copyright 2013 Wise Publications,
a division of Music Sales Limited.

Written, compiled and arranged by Justin Sandercoe.
Edited by Toby Knowles.
Design by Fresh Lemon.
Cover design by Paul Agar.
Cover photographs by Nick Delaney.
With thanks to Dario Cortese.
Printed in the EU.

Your Guarantee of Quality
As publishers, we strive to produce every book to the highest commercial standards.
This book has been carefully designed to minimise awkward page turns and to make playing
from it a real pleasure. Particular care has been given to specifying acid-free, neutral-sized
paper made from pulps which have not been elemental chlorine bleached. This pulp is from
farmed sustainable forests and was produced with special regard for the environment.
Throughout, the printing and binding have been planned to ensure a sturdy, attractive publication
which should give years of enjoyment. If your copy fails to meet our high standards, please
inform us and we will gladly replace it.

www.musicsales.com

www.justinguitar.com

STARTED LEARNED PERFORMED

Introduction

Beginner Stage — 8

☐☐☐ Give Peace A Chance — Plastic Ono Band — 10
☐☐☐ Bye Bye Love — The Everly Brothers — 12
☐☐☐ Be My Baby — The Ronettes — 14
☐☐☐ Band Of Gold — Freda Payne — 16
☐☐☐ Cherry, Cherry — Neil Diamond — 19
☐☐☐ Cecilia — Simon & Garfunkel — 22
☐☐☐ Catch The Wind — Donovan — 24
☐☐☐ All Day And All Of The Night — The Kinks — 27
☐☐☐ Make Me Smile (Come Up And See Me) — Steve Harley & Cockney Rebel — 30
☐☐☐ Sunny Afternoon — The Kinks — 33
☐☐☐ Summertime Blues — Eddie Cochran — 36
☐☐☐ Surfin' U.S.A. — The Beach Boys — 39
☐☐☐ Take It Easy — Eagles — 42
☐☐☐ The First Cut Is The Deepest — Cat Stevens — 45
☐☐☐ You've Got To Hide Your Love Away — The Beatles — 48

Intermediate Stage — 52

☐☐☐ All I Have To Do Is Dream — The Everly Brothers — 56
☐☐☐ Crying — Roy Orbison — 59
☐☐☐ Don't Let Me Be Misunderstood — The Animals — 62
☐☐☐ It's So Easy — Buddy Holly — 65
☐☐☐ I Feel Fine — The Beatles — 68
☐☐☐ In My Life — The Beatles — 71
☐☐☐ I Heard It Through The Grapevine — Marvin Gaye — 74
☐☐☐ I Shot The Sheriff — Bob Marley — 77
☐☐☐ Love Me Tender — Elvis Presley — 80
☐☐☐ Sweet Caroline — Neil Diamond — 82
☐☐☐ Suspicious Minds — Elvis Presley — 84
☐☐☐ The Weight — The Band — 87
☐☐☐ Try A Little Tenderness — Otis Redding — 90
☐☐☐ Unchained Melody — The Righteous Brothers — 93
☐☐☐ Angie — The Rolling Stones — 96

INTRODUCTION

 ## Welcome to my Vintage Songbook!

This book is for guitar players who have worked through the basics of playing, and are now aiming to progress beyond beginner level. I expect many of you will have completed my free online Beginner's Guitar Course and perhaps learned songs from the Justinguitar.com Beginner's Songbook. This book continues on from there and introduces material used in the Intermediate Method (also free on the website), including barre chords and sixteenth-note strumming.

There are four sections to the book, starting with a 'Beginner' section, and ending with a section of full TAB transcriptions. The Beginner section mainly uses chords, rhythms and techniques covered in my Beginner's Guitar Course, with a few new tricks thrown in to keep things interesting. It's a great selection of tunes, which are fun to play, not too tricky to master, and which will help you consolidate your knowledge.

The 'Intermediate' section introduces barre chords. Playing barre chords is probably the most important skill to learn, after you've become confident with all your beginner techniques. Some songs use only barre chords, while others mix them with open chords—you'll need to master both approaches. If you are uncertain about how to play barre chords, please check out the relevant lessons on the website.

Next up we have 'Intermediate Plus' which, as the name suggests, uses many of the skills and techniques covered in the Intermediate Method but adds some other interesting elements, such as new chords, more complex rhythm patterns and riffs.

Lastly, we have five full guitar TAB transcriptions, which should prove a little more challenging and give you something to work towards! They are almost all instrumental and go from very possible for intermediate players ('Apache') to very difficult for everyone (''Cause We Ended As Lovers') so they should take you from fun to pulling your hair out!

I'd like to thank Toby and Tom at Music Sales for their help and suggestions, and also the many website users that offered song suggestions. Thanks also to Jed Wardley for helping get this book to you, Dario Cortese for his help proofreading, transcribing and general counsel and to the forum moderators (Tom, Lieven, Jonathan and Richard) for their massive contribution to our community.

If you enjoy this book then you might like to keep an eye out for others in this series, which include a range of styles including rock, pop and acoustic. I hope you enjoy playing the songs in this book and wish you a lot of joy on your musical journey.

Justin Sandercoe
November 2013, London

If you get stuck with anything in this songbook then your first port of call should be my website where there are many hundreds of completely free lessons that will take you from complete novice level to wherever you want to go!

www.justinguitar.com

If you enjoy online interaction there is a great forum where there are many thousands of students helping each other every day! It really is a passionate, supportive and active community, and you are welcome to join it.

www.justinguitarcommunity.com

PRACTICE GUIDE

 Top 10 Practice Tips

1. Practise what you can't do, not what you can.

2. Practice makes permanent (not perfect). So get it right!

3. Start slowly and get it right before you speed up.

4. Using a timer saves time.

5. Focus on one element of a song at a time.

6. Try to practise a little every day, rather than a lot all on one day.

7. Keep track of your practice: use a practice schedule.

8. If it sounds good, it is good!

9. Playing and Practising are very different—don't confuse them.

10. The more you think, the more you stink! Practise until the part becomes instinctive.

 Using Software

I would strongly suggest getting some software that will allow you to change the speed of a recording but not the pitch. I use one called Transcribe! but there are many others available, including Audacity, Capo and the Amazing Slow Downer.

Set the software to play the song at 50%, or at whatever speed you can practise in time with. Play along with the recording; use the 'cycle' feature to repeat one section (or the whole song) over and over. Once you are confident that you can play this section precisely, speed the track up, a little bit at a time. This may happen over the course of a few weeks, or in one practice session, depending on your ability and on the difficulty of the song.

Take time to learn how to use the software, in particular how to use the key commands (keyboard shortcuts). This will save you countless hours!

✿ Practising Harder Material

When approaching a more complex song, start by having a mess around—play through the song a few times as well as you can, working out where the tricky bits are, and which sections will require the most attention. Pick one section and play it very slowly and accurately—I usually start with the main riff or theme, or perhaps the introduction. Make sure that you get it right. Every time you play something wrong you are entering 'bad code' into your brain.

Try to play this section with the correct rhythm, even if it is very slow. I recommend that you count out the beats while you're practising, as this will help a lot. Don't worry about the groove just yet, but concentrate on precision, making sure that your timing is mathematically correct.

Try to get this first 'chunk' into your memory as soon as you can. Your goal should be to play while looking at your guitar (or closing your eyes), rather than following the music on the page. After you have memorised this first 'chunk', you should build upon it. Learn the next section, slowly and carefully, and once you can play this new section in time (no matter how slowly), join it on to the first section. Work on creating a flow between the two sections, and practise both sections 'joined-up' until you can play them at 70-80% of the actual speed of the song.

Continue this process until you can play through the whole song at a slower tempo, and then start to speed the tempo up, until you can play at full speed. It's much better to play correctly at a slower tempo than to play at full speed, with mistakes. If there are one or two extra hard bits, extract them and work on them on their own. When they are sounding good enough, put them back into the whole song.

BEGINNER STAGE

Beginner

Intermediate

Intermediate +

TAB

 ## Introduction

This first chapter mainly uses the chords, rhythms and techniques covered in my Beginner's Course. The layout is the same as in my Beginner's Songbook, with chords and lyrics on one page and tips and rhythms on the facing page.

 ## Chords

For the most part, the chords used in this section are the eight essential open chords:

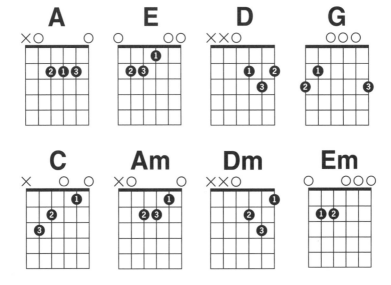

You'll also find a few variations of these and some basic slash chords.

 ## F Chord

I assume that you are also familiar with the F chord. Below left is the full barre version of the chord, and on the right is the smaller, simpler version of the chord.

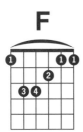

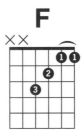

Beginner

Intermediate

Intermediate +

TAB

 ## 7th Chords

We'll also be using these (dominant) 7th chords, which are also open chords, as shown below.

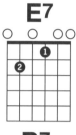

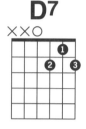

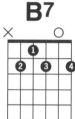
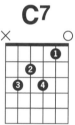
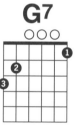

 ## Sus Chords

Lastly, we'll be playing a few sus chords, which again are nice, friendly open chords.

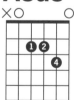

9

Give Peace A Chance

Words & Music by John Lennon

Capo Fret **1**

Beginner

Intermediate

Intermediate +

TAB

Intro

N.C.
Two, one, two , three, four.

| C | C | C | C |

Verse 1

C
Ev'rybody's talking about
C
Bagism, Shagism,
C
Dragism, Madism,
C
Ragism, Tagism,
C
Thisism, Thatism.
C   C
Isn't it the most?

Chorus 1

C   G7   G7   G7
All we are saying,
  G7   C   C   C
Is give peace a chance.
C   G7   G7   G7
All we are saying,
  G7   C
Is give peace a chance.

Verse 2

Ev'rybody's talking about
Ministers, Sinisters,
Banisters and Canisters,
Bishops and Fishops and
Rabbis and Popeyes,
Bye bye bye byes.

Chorus 2

As Chorus 1

Verse 3

Ev'rybody's talking about
Revolution, Evolution,
Mastication, Flagelation,
Regulations, Integrations,
Meditations, United Nations,
Congratulations.

Chorus 3

As Chorus 1

Beginner

Intermediate

Intermediate +

TAB

Verse 4

Ev'rybody's talking about
John and Yoko, Timmy Leary,
Rosemary, Tommy Smothers,
Bobby Dylan, Tommy Cooper,
Derek Taylor, Norman Mailer,
Alan Ginsberg, Hare Krishna,
Hare, Hare Krishna.

 Introduction

John Lennon's first solo single, released by The Plastic Ono Band came out
in 1969 and was written and recorded during the second of Lennon's famous
bed-ins.

 Strumming

This has got to be one of the easiest songs of all time—it's got just two
chords: C and G7. The thing to capture is the spirit and feeling of the
groove which is far harder than the chords!

There are many variations during the song but it loosely follows this
two-bar pattern:

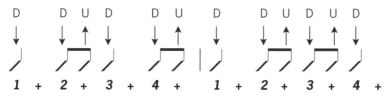

Don't be worried if the rhythm pattern varies a bit—it does on the
recording and it's really not important in this kind of song to play the
pattern absolutely consistently.

One thing you might like to try (and which was a party favourite when
I was growing up) is playing the song and making up your own words
for the verses—it can be a real laugh and is definitely in the right spirit
of the song!

Bye Bye Love

Words & Music by Felice Bryant & Boudleaux Bryant

Beginner

Intermediate

Intermediate +

TAB

Intro

| A5   C5 D5 | A |

| A   C5 D5 | A |

Chorus 1

D   A
Bye bye love,

D   A
Bye bye happiness,

D   A
  Hello loneliness,

|A   E |A
I think I'm a-gonna cry.

D   A
Bye bye love,

D   A
Bye bye sweet caress,

D   A
  Hello emptiness,

|A   E |A
I feel like I could die.

  |A   E |A
Bye bye my love, goodbye.

Verse 1

N.C.   E   E   A   A
There goes my baby   with someone new,

           E   E   A   A7
She sure looks happy, I sure am blue.

         D   D   E   E
She was my baby 'til he stepped in,

         E   E   A   A7
Goodbye to romance that might have been.

Chorus 2

As Chorus 1

Verse 2

I'm a-through with romance
I'm a-through with love
I'm through with a-countin' the stars above
And there's a reason that I'm so free:
My lovin' baby is a-through with me.

Chorus 2

As Chorus 1

Outro

   |A   E |A
Bye bye my love goodbye...   (*Repeat to Fade*)

Introduction

This song was a huge hit for The Everly Brothers way back in 1957.

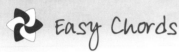

Easy Chords

This song mainly consists of just three chords (as well as a sneaky C in the intro riff and some 7th chords which can be left out if you don't know them) and is loads of fun to play. You'll hear on the original recording that the intro uses an A5 chord followed by power chords on C and D; however you can play regular open chords instead—it will still sound close to the original. You'll also hear some muted strings being hit. To recreate this, just rest all of your (fretting-hand) fingers lightly on the strings and strum!

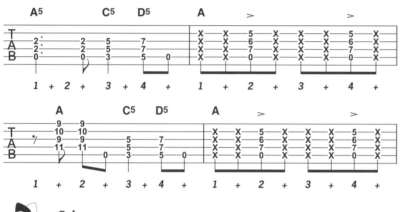

Strumming

The strumming pattern as played by The Everly Brothers is very simple and your practice time should be spent making it feel good, and making it really 'swing'.

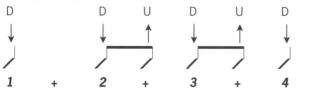

When there are two chords per bar, the pattern varies slightly to:

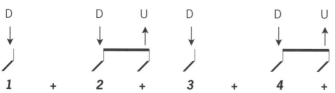

13

Be My Baby

Words & Music by Jeff Barry, Ellie Greenwich & Phil Spector

Capo Fret 4

Beginner

Intermediate

Intermediate +

TAB

Intro

drums 2 bars | C | C |

Verse 1

C   C
The night we met I knew I
Dm   G7
Needed you so,
C   C
And if I had the chance I'd
Dm   G7
Never let you go
E7   E7
So won't you say love me?
A7   A7
I'll make you so proud of me.
D7   D7
We'll make them turn their heads
G   G7
Every place we go...

Chorus

           C   C
...So won't you please *(Be my, be my baby)*,
      Am   Am
Be my little baby *(My one and only baby)*,
         F   F
Say you'll be my darling *(Be my, be my baby)*,
      G7   G7
Be my baby now *(My one and only baby)*.

Verse 2

I'll make you happy baby,
Just wait and see.
For every kiss you give me,
I'll give you three.
Since the day I saw you,
I have been waiting for you,
You know I will adore you to eternity.

Chorus 2

As Chorus 1

Instr.

‖: C | C | Dm | G7 :‖

                  2° So come on and please...

Chorus 3

As Chorus 1

Link

drums 2 bars

Chorus 4

Repeat Chorus to fade

14

Introduction

This song, produced by the legendary Phil Spector, was a huge hit for The Ronettes in 1963 and is considered to be one of the greatest pop records ever made. It is a textbook example of great pop songwriting and arranging.

Chords

This song is easy and really rewarding for beginner players. I've arranged it for open chords by putting a capo at the 4th fret. I suspect the original was played using barre chords all the way through and perhaps once you get into the Intermediate Method (on my website) you might like to play it using all barre chords—the substitutions are shown below. This chord sequence is really 'of its time'—all those 7th chords really move the song along and theory nerds might like to look up 'secondary dominants' to understand what is going on harmonically. To play it without a capo, substitute the chords as shown on the chart below—you will have to use barre chords for most of them!

WRITTEN CHORD (capo 4)	ACTUAL PITCH
C	E
D^7, Dm	F$^{\sharp}$7, F$^{\sharp}$m
E^7	G$^{\sharp}$7
F	A
G, G^7	B, B^7
A^7, Am	C$^{\sharp}$7, C$^{\sharp}$m

Strumming

This is a good song for exploring different strumming patterns. The pattern that I call 'Old Faithful' will sound great, but you really should experiment and see what feels good for you. This little variation of 'Old Faithful' works great too—adding that last up-strum just helps keep it moving.

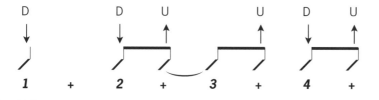

Band Of Gold

Words & Music by Ronald Dunbar & Edith Wayne

Beginner

Intermediate

Intermediate +

TAB

Intro

riff
| (G) | (G) | G | G | |

Chorus 1

                G
Now that you're gone
G   D
All that's left is a band of gold.
D   C
All that's left of the dreams I hold
    C
Is a band of gold
        G/B   C
And the memories of what love could be
    G/B   C/D
If you are still here with me.

Verse 1

(chords as Chorus)

You took me from the shelter of a mother I had never known
Who loved any other.
We kissed after taking vows, but that night on our honeymoon
We stayed in separate rooms.

Verse 2

I wait in the darkness of my lonely room
Filled with sadness, filled with gloom.
Hoping soon that you'll walk back through that door
And love me like you tried before.

Chorus 2

Since you've been gone
All that's left is a band of gold.
All that's left of the dreams I hold
Is a band of gold
And the dream of what love could be
If you were still here with me.

Instrumental

| G | G | D | D | C | C | |
riff
| (G) | (G) | G | G | |

Verse 3

Ooh, don't you know that
I wait in the darkness of my lonely room
Filled with sadness, filled with gloom.
Hoping soon that you'll walk back through that door
And love me like you tried before.

Chorus 3

As Chorus 2 *(Repeat to Fade)*

 ## Introduction

This song was a big hit for Freda Payne in 1970. It was written by the great songwriting team of Holland–Dozier–Holland (under a pseudonym) and recorded with legendary session band The Funk Brothers.

 ## Chord Options

You have a few options for the chords in this song. As a beginner you should use simple open chords and a strumming pattern like 'Old Faithful' (see p.35) but those progressing onwards might like to try a more Motown approach and use the same chord grip moving around the neck.

This version of the G Chord is the same as the 'small F' that we learned in the Beginner Course but up two frets. Moving the shape up so your 1st finger is on the 8th fret will give you a C Chord, and at the 10th fret it will give you a D Chord. Pretty cool, huh? Just make sure you don't play the thickest two strings, and maybe even keep them muted with the heel of your strumming hand.

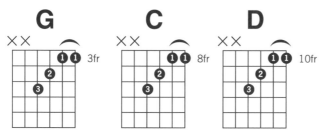

For the G/B and C/D chords there are some new grips you can try, but if you struggle with them, remember that you can leave out the bass note (the note written after the /) and just play the standard chords of G and C.

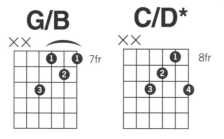

* Alright, it's not precisely a C/D but it's what was used commonly at the time as a C/D because the bass player would be playing the bass note!

Beginner

Intermediate

Intermediate +

TAB

 Rhythm

The rhythm guitar part is hard to identify on the original recording, but to my ears it sounds like it is playing the pattern below, with a few variations. This pattern is quite tricky for a beginner, so you may want to use some 'chips' instead, playing them on every strong beat (see the Intermediate Course, lesson IM-155). In any event, It's best to listen, play along, experiment and see what you find!

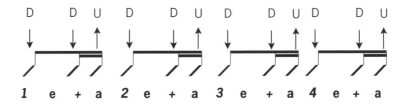

Riff

Also in this song is a cool little guitar riff you might like to check out, which happens in the intro and later in the instrumental section.

Cherry, Cherry
Words & Music by Neil Diamond

Beginner

Intermediate

Intermediate +

TAB

 ## Introduction

This song was Neil Diamond's first big hit, released in 1966, just a few months before The Monkees covered his song 'I'm A Believer' and propelled him to superstardom.

 ## Strumming

This song has a great rhythm guitar part that really drives the song along. It's the kind of part that is best learned slowly and carefully before you decide to speed it up. Your real focus should be on the accents—you have to get the chord changes in the right place of course, but it's the accents that will really bring out the groove and make the rhythm part so recognisable.

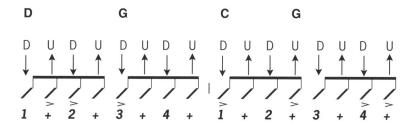

In the Bridge the chords change and the rhythm loses the accent pattern but check out the pushed D chord (half a beat early!) which changes the rhythmic feel and fits with the riff on the next page.

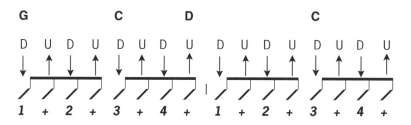

Cherry, Cherry

Words & Music by Neil Diamond

Capo Fret 1

Beginner

Intermediate

Intermediate +

TAB

Intro

‖: D G | C G | D G | D G :‖

Verse 1

|D   G |C G |D G|C G
    Baby loves me, yes, yes she does,

     |D   G |C G|D G|C G|
Ah, the girl's outta sight, yeah.

|D   G |C G |D G|C G
Says she loves me, yes, yes she does,

     |D   G |C G |
Mmm, gonna show me to - night, yeah.

Chorus 1

|D   G |C   G |
She got the way to move me, Cherry,

|D   G |C   G |
She got the way to groove me.

|D   G |C   G |D
She got the way to move me,   Cherry baby,

     G |C   D |
She got the way to groove me, all right.

Link 1

| (G) (C) | (D) (C) | G C | D C |

Bridge 1

|G   C |D   C |G   C|D C |
Tell___ your mama, girl, I can't stay long,

|G C |D   C |G   C|D C |
We got things we gotta catch up on.

|G   C |D   C |G   C|D C |
Mmm, you know, you know what I'm saying,

|G   C |D   C |G   C|D C |
Can't stand still while the music is playing.

Link 2

| D G | C G | D G | C G |
        All right.

Verse 2

You ain't got no right, no, no you don't,
Ah, to be so exciting.
Won't need bright lights, no, no we won't,
Mmm, gonna make our own lightning.

Chorus 2

As Chorus 1

Link 3

As Link 1

Bridge 2　　No, we won't tell a soul where we going to,
Girl, we do whatever we want to.
Ah, I love the way that you do me,
Cherry, babe, you really get to me.

Link 4　　As Link 2

Chorus 3　　As Chorus 1　*(Repeat to Fade)*

Riff

As well as the catchy rhythm part there is a cool little riff that comes
during the Link before the Bridge sections, and which you might like to
play as a break from the rhythm.

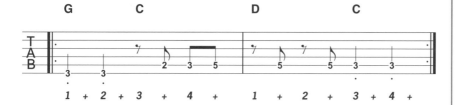

21

Cecilia

Words & Music by Paul Simon

Beginner

Intermediate

Intermediate +

TAB

Intro   **Percussion for 4 bars**

Chorus 1

N.C.
Cecilia, you're breaking my heart,
                         |G
You're shaking my confidence daily.
      |F C |F   C
Oh Ce - cilia, I'm down on my knees,
      |F   C |G |
I'm begging you please to come home.

Chorus 2

|C |F   C
Cecilia, you're breaking my heart,
  |F   C |G
You're shaking my confidence daily.
      |F C |F   C
Oh Cecilia, I'm down on my knees,
     |F   C |G
I'm begging you please to come home,
        C
Come on home.

Verse 1

C |F   C |C
  Making love in the after - noon with Cecilia
F   C |G   C |
Up in my bed - room,
C |F   C
  I got up to wash my face.
       |C   F   C |G   C |
When I come back to bed, someone's taken my place.

Chorus 3   As Chorus 2

Link

N.C.   G
Oh oh oh oh oh, oh oh oh oh oh, oh oh oh-oh.

| C | | F | C | F | C | G | |
| F | C | F | C | F | C | G | |

Chorus 4

     |F C |F   C
Jubila - tion, she loves me a - gain,
 |F   C |G
I fall on the floor and I'm lau - ghing,
     |F C |F   C
Jubila - tion, she loves me a - gain,
 |F   C |G
I fall on the floor and I'm lau - ghing.

Coda

```
        |F C     |F       C
|: Oh oh oh oh, oh oh oh oh oh
   |F      C     |G
Oh oh oh oh oh oh oh oh oh. :|   Repeat to fade
```

Introduction

This awesome tune was released by Simon & Garfunkel on their magnificent final album *Bridge Over Troubled Water* (1970).

Rhythm

Rhythm plays a very big part in this song—one cool thing you can try for the intro is hitting the heel of your palm onto the body of your acoustic guitar to get a big 'kick drum' sound. Don't hit it hard enough to damage your guitar—make it a positive thud but don't whack it too aggressively! Once the rhythm guitar comes in there are many rhythmic variations, but the main vibe for strumming is shown below.

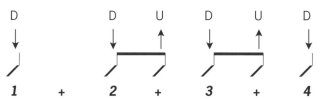

You'll also hear some 'melodic' variations, where melody lines are echoed in the bass lines, like in the example shown below. Because there's no set rhythm pattern, you can experiment with these ideas and use them in other sections of the song. We've taken the example from 1:38 of the track, which occurs at the first C chord of the Link section.

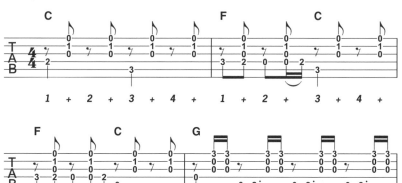

Beginner

Intermediate

Intermediate +

TAB

23

Catch The Wind

Words & Music by Donovan Leitch

Capo Fret 3

Intro $\begin{smallmatrix}6\\8\end{smallmatrix}$| C | Fadd9   G | C   Fadd9 | C |

Verse 1

        C   Fadd9
In the chilly hours and minutes

          C   F
Of uncertainty, I   want to be

C | Fadd9   G | C | G7 |
In the warm hold of your lovin' mind,

         C   Fadd9
To feel you all around me

          C   F
And to take your hand along the sand,

C | Fadd9   G | C   Fadd9 | C |
Ah, but I may as well try and catch the wind.

Verse 2

When sundown pales the sky,
I want to hide a while behind your smile
And everywhere I'd look, your eyes I'd find.
For me to love you now
Would be the sweetest thing, t'would make me sing,
Ah, but I may as well try and catch the wind.

Instrumental | F | Em | F |

                   | D/F♯ | G   G/E | G/F   G/E |

Verse 3

When rain has hung the leaves with tears
I want you near to kill my fears,
To help me to leave all my   blues behind.
For standin' in your heart
Is where I want to be   and long to be,
Ah, but I may as well try and catch the wind.

Solo | C | Fadd9 | C | F |

      | C | Fadd9   G | C | G7 |

      | C | Fadd9 | C | F |

      | C | Fadd9   G | C   Fadd9 | C |

Outro | C | Fadd9 | C | F |

       C | Fadd9   G | C   Fadd9 | C |
Ah, but I may as well try and catch the wind.

Beginner

Intermediate

Intermediate +

TAB

Introduction

This folk-pop song was a hit for Donovan in 1965. This song is in 6/8 time, meaning there are two 'pulses' per bar, each of which is divided into three beats. When strumming, the usual approach is to play all six beats with down-strums and add in up-strums where needed.

 ## Intro

The intro is a lesson in 1960s folk guitar playing, where the bass notes are picked out to form a melodic line, while the strums are played in between. Remember that all the strong beats will take down-strums, while the '+'s will take up-strums. This kind of groove takes practice to master but once you've got it, you can transfer the technique to other songs that are in a similar style. So take your time and make sure you play those bass notes accurately! Notice that for the whole of the intro, you'll be keeping your little finger on fret 3 of the thinnest string.

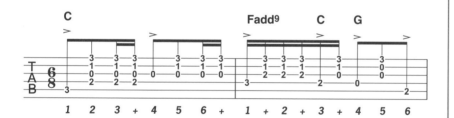

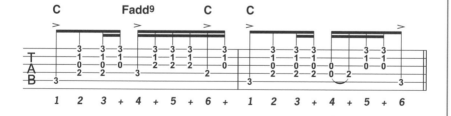

continued...

Beginner

Intermediate

Intermediate +

TAB

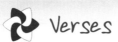 Verses

The verses use much the same technique as the intro—a combination of bass notes and chords—though the guitar part is simpler, with bass notes on 1 and 4, while the up-strums are more occasional. I'd recommend starting by using all-down strums, and letting the up-strums fall into place on their own as you get a feel for the pattern.

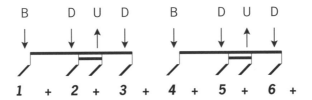

There is a variation at the end of each phrase of the verses, which is slightly harder as the G7 chord change is not quite where you expect it to be!

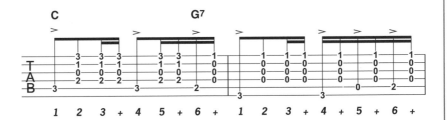

 Chords

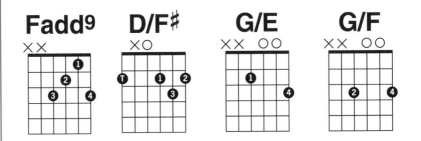

26

All Day And All Of The Night
Words & Music by Ray Davies

 Introduction

This song was a big hit for The Kinks in 1964, and was taken back into the Top Ten by The Stranglers over 20 years later. In this tutorial we're looking at the original Kinks version.

 Power Chords Or Barres?

This song is great for working on your power chords and E-shape barre chords. As it's in the Beginner section I'm presenting the chords as power chords, but when the time comes to start working on your barre chords, you should return to this song, trying it out with full major barre chords.

One really interesting thing about the 1960s guitar chord 'vocabulary' is that it was common to stay with the same chord grip, sometimes moving it right up the neck. In this song you will stay with a sixth string root for all the chords, except for the B♭ at the start of the pre-chorus, for which you use a fifth string root. The same rule will apply for both power chords and barre chords in this song! You can confirm this for yourself by watching one of the early televised live performances of the song such as the one on the *Shindig* show in 1965 (which includes an amusing minor mistake: a wrong chord at about 01:06, after which you can see a knowing wink from the lead guitarist, Dave Davies).

Riff 1 (Verse)

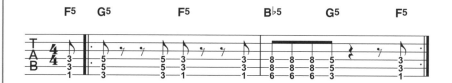

27

All Day And All Of The Night

Words & Music by Ray Davies

Beginner

Intermediate

Intermediate +

TAB

Intro

riff 1

F5 ‖: G5 F5 | B♭5 G5 F5 :‖

Verse 1

riff 1 x4
I'm not content to be with you in the daytime.
Girl I want to be with you all of the time.

Pre-Chorus 1

B♭5　　　　F5　　　　　　|A5　　　G5 |C5　A5　|
The only time I feel alright is by your side.

Chorus 1

|D5　C5　　　|F5　　　D5　　　|D5
Girl I want to be with you all of the time
　　C5　　　|F5　　　D5　　|
All day and all of the night,
|D5　C5　　　|F5　　　D5　　|
　All day and all of the night,
|D5　C5　　　|F5　　　D5　　|
　All day and all of the night.

Verse 2

I believe that you and me last forever,
Oh yeah, all day and night time yours, leave me never.

Pre-Chorus 2

B♭5　　　　F5　　　　　　|A5　　　G5 |C5　A5　|
The only time I feel alright is by your side.

Chorus 2

Girl I want to be with you all of the time
All day and all of the night,
All day and all of the night.

Link

| D5　C5 |F5　　| F5　　| D5　　| D5　　　　|
　　　　　　　　　　　　　　　　　Oh, come on...

Solo

‖: G5 F5 | B♭5 G5 F5 :‖ *(Play x5)*

Verse 3

As Verse 2

Chorus 3

As Chorus 1

Coda

| D5　C5 | F5　　D5　　|

28

Riffs 2 + 3

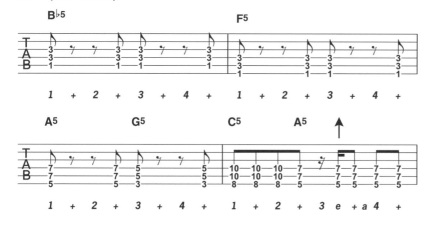

Riff 2 (Pre-chorus)

Riff 3 (Chorus)

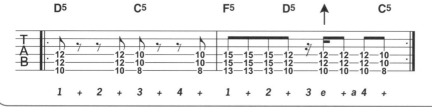

Rhythm

I would recommend using all down-strums for the rhythm of this song, with the exception of two up-strums, which I have marked on the TAB. This will help your playing sound authentic and energetic.

There are a lot of fast chord changes in the song, so one thing you should be aware of is releasing the pressure when you move a chord shape. Try to keep your fingers in the right place but relax the pressure before you move your chord grip up or down the fretboard. Pressure will make it slower to move your chord grip to its next position, and therefore slower to change chord, whilst a relaxed, loose grip will not!

Make Me Smile (Come Up And See Me)

Words & Music by Steve Harley

Beginner

Intermediate

Intermediate +

TAB

Intro

| (G) | (G) | (G) |

Verse 1

N.C.   F   C   G
You've done it all: you've broken every code,
F   C   G   G   G
   And pulled the rebel to the floor.
                   F   C   G
You've spoilt the game, no matter what you say,
F   C   G   G
   For only metal, what a bore.
F   C
   Blue eyes,   blue eyes,
F   C   G   G
   How can you tell so many lies?

Chorus 1

Dm   F   C   G
   Come up and see me, make me smile,
Dm   F   C   G   G   N.C.
   I'll do what you want, running wild.

Verse 2

There's nothing left, all gone and run away.
Maybe you'll tarry for a while.
It's just a test, a game for us to play,
Win or lose, it's hard to smile.
Resist, resist:
It's from yourself you'll have to hide.

Chorus 2

As Chorus 1

Guitar solo

F	Em	F	Am
Em	Em	G	G
Dm	F	C	G
Dm	F	C	G	G	N.C.

Verse 3

There ain't no more: you've taken everything
From my belief in Mother Earth
Can you ignore my faith in everything?
'Cause I know what faith is and what it's worth.
Away, away,
And don't say maybe you'll try, oh, oh.

Chorus 3

As Chorus 1

Link 1	| F	| C	| F	| C	| G	| G	|
Chorus 4	As Chorus 1						
Link 2	| F	| C	| F	| C	| G	| G	|
Chorus 5	As Chorus 1 *(Repeat to Fade)*						

Introduction

This song was a massive hit for Steve Harley & Cockney Rebel in 1975, and features a great acoustic solo by guitarist Jim Cregan.

Rhythm

There are quite a few chords in this song, but they are standard grips and the rhythm is not particularly tricky either, making this a great song for a beginner. As far as I can tell it mostly uses the rhythm pattern shown below, but 'Old Faithful' works just as well.

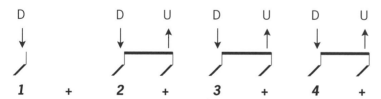

One thing to watch out for is the stops and starts! You'll have to count out loud to get them, which can be tricky for a band, who all need to come in tight together—if you watch the video (on YouTube) of Cockney Rebel performing live on *Top Of The Pops*, you can see them all enjoying the challenge with a wink and a smile!

continued…

Beginner

Intermediate

Intermediate +

TAB

Intro

There is a nice intro to learn too, which makes the song instantly recognisable. It's basically just an ascending C Major scale, starting on a G (for you theory fans, that's a G Mixolydian scale).

G

```
T
A
B
    3  5
       2  3  5
             2  3  5
                   2  4  5  4 (4)
                                  5
                                     2  4  5  4  ⁇  2  4
```

1 + 2 + 3 + 4 +   1 + 2 + 3 + 4 +   1 + 2 + 3 + 4 +

Solo

The solo in this song is lovely too—I remember learning it as a teenager and struggling with the faster runs, but all in all it's a nice one to play. Jim Cregan is a fantastic guitar player with a great sense of melody. Have a listen and see if you pick out a few of the easier licks—it'll be worth the effort!

Sunny Afternoon

Words & Music by Ray Davies

 ## Introduction

This is the Kinks' wonderfully catchy song about the horrors of taxation and the hard life that follows after paying your share!

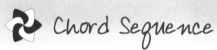

Chord Sequence

As well as just generally being a great fun song to play, there is a wonderful sequence of chords, built on a descending bass part, which I'm sure you'll enjoy. The chords can be a little tricky to play but are well worth the effort. Follow the fingering exactly as shown and take the changes slowly at first in order to get your fingers used to them. Note that for many of the chords you will have to mute one or more strings with your fretting-hand fingers, usually with the underside of a finger fretting a note. For example, when playing the Dm/C, finger 3 will lightly touch (and therefore mute) the fourth string while playing the fifth string!

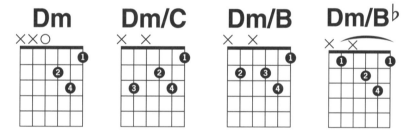

Dm **Dm/C** **Dm/B** **Dm/B♭**

In the Dm/B♭ you'll need to use a 'bridging barre' where your finger will be 'rounder' than a usual barre, so that it will mute the fourth string. You'll be fretting the tip down on the fifth string and fretting the first (thinnest) string with the underside, while the rest of your barre will bridge over the rest of the strings, and which will mute the fourth string. It can be a little tricky but is a very useful technique to learn. The A/F is commonly played like a regular A but with the added bass note played by your thumb—that would be my preferred method, but I know many of you might struggle with that so I have written a no thumb alternative for you in the chord boxes!

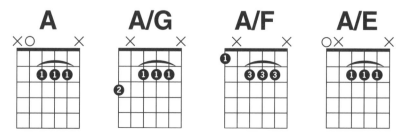

A **A/G** **A/F** **A/E**

33

Sunny Afternoon

Words & Music by Ray Davies

Intro

‖: Dm   Dm/C |Dm/B   Dm/B♭ |A   A/G |A/F A/E :‖

Verse 1

         Dm   C
Well, the taxman's taken all my dough,
       F   C7
And left me in my stately home,
|A   A/G |A/F A/E |Dm
Lazing on a sunny after - noon,
          C
And I can't sail my yacht,
     F   C7
He's taken every - thing I've got,   **(Bass)**
|A   A/G |A/F A/E |Dm |Dm (A) (B) (C♯) |
All I've got's this sunny after - noon.   (Oh,)

Bridge 1

     D7   D7   G7   G7
Oh, save me, save me, save me from this squeeze,
       C7   C7   F   A7
I've got a big fat Mama tryin' to break me.

Chorus 1

      Dm   G7
And I love to live so pleasantly,
Dm |G7 C7|
Live this life of luxu - ry,
F   A7 |Dm Dm/C |Dm/B Dm/B♭
Lazing on a sunny after - noon.
   |A   A/G |A/F A/E
In the summer - time,
   |Dm   Dm/C|Dm/B Dm/B♭
In the summer - time,
   |A   A/G|A/F A/E |
In the summer - time.

Verse 2

My girlfriend's run off with my car,
And gone back to her Ma and Pa,
Telling tales of drunkenness and cruelty.
Now I'm sitting here,
Sipping at my ice cold beer,
Lazing on a sunny afternoon.

Bridge 2

Help me, help me, help me sail away,
Well give me two good reasons why I oughta stay.

Chorus 2

As Chorus 1

Bridge 3

As Bridge 1

Chorus 3   As Chorus 1

Outro   In the summertime...in the summertime...

‖: Dm   :‖   *Repeat to fade*

✿ Strumming

The rhythm patterns for this song will alternate between 4 down-strums on the beat, played very tight, perhaps even using some muting between the strums, and 'Old Faithful'. You can hear the different patterns quite clearly on the recording so it will be easiest if you follow that along.

Down-strums on the beat

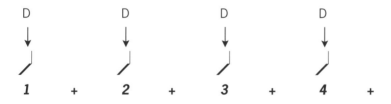

'Old Faithful'

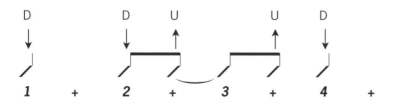

Summertime Blues

Words & Music by Eddie Cochran & Jerry Capehart

Beginner

Intermediate

Intermediate +

TAB

Intro

| E   A | B7   E | E   A | B7   E |

Verse 1

      E   E
I'm a-gonna raise a fuss, I'm a-gonna raise a holler,

| E   A | B7   E |

        E   E
About a-workin' all summer just to try to earn a dollar.

| E   A | B7   E |

        A   A
Ev'ry time I call my baby, try to get a date,

        N.C.   N.C.
My boss says, 'No dice, son, you gotta work late,'

Chorus 1

A |A
Sometimes I wonder what I'm a-gonna do,

          E (N.C.)   E   E
But there ain't no cure for the summertime blues.

Link 1

| E   A | B7   E | E   A | B7   E |

Verse 2

A-well my Mom 'n' Papa told me,
'Son, you gotta make some money,
If you want-ta use the car to go a-ridin' next Sunday.'
Well, I didn't go to work, told the boss I was sick,
'Now you can't use the car 'cause you didn't work a lick.'

Chorus 2

As Chorus 1

Verse 3

I'm gonna take two weeks, gonna have a fine vacation,
I'm gonna take my problems to the United Nations!
Well, I called my Congressman and he said (quote),
'I'd like to help you, son, but you're too young to vote.'

Chorus 3

As Chorus 1

Outro

| E   A | B7   E | E   A | B7   E | *(Repeat to fade)*

Introduction

Eddie Cochran's rock 'n' roll hit from 1958 has a very memorable rhythm guitar part and is dead easy to play!

 ## Rhythm Riff

'Summertime Blues' has a great groove and uses nice, easy open chords. It uses some palm muting and eighth-note strumming to keep things rocking, and consequently getting the rhythm right is the most important thing. On the original recording, the acoustic guitar parts are just strumming the main riff, while an electric guitar plays the bass note riff.

Below is a TAB arrangement of the main riff—notice the X's which signify the muted strings. To get these sounding cool you should leave your chord in position but relax the fingers and reposition them ever so slightly, so that all the strings are muted—although for these muted strums you should be really be focusing on the thicker strings.

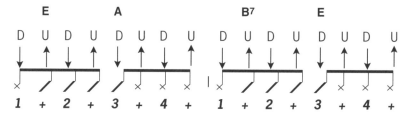

 ## Rock 'n' Roll Riff

On the A chord in the chorus, it'll sound nice and authentic if you add a little 12-bar rock 'n' roll flavour to it, like this:

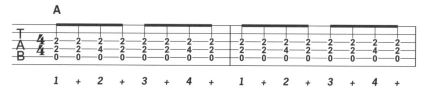

Once you've got the groove on, the only thing to watch out for is the stops!

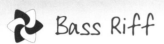 Bass Riff

The bass note riff, which you'll hear clearly during the intro, is played by picking close to the bridge. There is a cool step-up on the E, while the rest of the riff just follows the chords, using even eighth-notes!

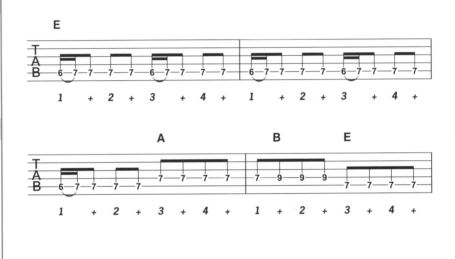

Surfin' U.S.A.

Words by Brian Wilson, Music by Chuck Berry

 ## Introduction

This is the all-time classic Beach Boys single from 1963, which borrows the chords and melody of Chuck Berry's earlier hit, 'Sweet Little Sixteen'.

 ## Which Way To Play?

This is one of those songs that you can play many different ways, depending on your technical ability. To start you can just use simple open chords and a solid rhythm pattern as shown below. Remember that in the verses you have a stop every second bar, but in the chorus you should just keep repeating the rhythm that is shown in bar 1. Remember to count out the rests if you are unsure how long to stop for—and if you can, try to tap your foot and sing the words along!

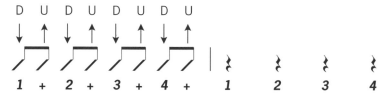

 ## Intro

There is also a classic electric guitar intro to learn—it's not hard and sets the mood right away, so it's certainly worth checking out! Make sure you hold down both a mini-barre and finger 2 all the way through—that way you'll only have to move finger 3 around. Use down-strums throughout.

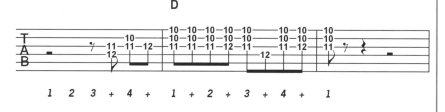

Surfin' U.S.A.

Words by Brian Wilson, Music by Chuck Berry

Capo
Fret

1

Intermediate

Intermediate +

TAB

Intro

| D |

Verse 1

N.C.   A
If everybody had an ocean,
N.C.   D
Across the U.S.A.
N.C.   A
Then everybody'd be surfin',
N.C.   D
Like Californ.I.A.
N.C.   G
You'd seem 'em wearing their baggies,
N.C.   D
Huarachi sandals too.
N.C.   A |G   N.C.
A bushy bushy blonde hairdo,
            |D
Surfin' U.S.A.

Chorus 1

D   A
  You'll catch 'em surfin' at Del Mar,
A   D
  Ventura County line.
D   A
  Santa Cruz and Trestle,
A   D
  Australia's Narrabeen.
D   G
  All over Man - hattan,
G   D
  And down Doheny Way.
D   A |G N.C.
  Everybody's gone surfin',
            |D
Surfin' U.S.A.

Verse 2

We'll all be planning out a route,
We're gonna take real soon.
We're waxing down our surfboards,
We can't wait for June.
We'll all be gone for the summer,
We're on safari to stay.
Tell the teacher we're surfin',
Surfin' U.S.A.

Chorus 2

Haggerties and Swamies,
Pacific Palisades.
San Onofre and Sunset,
Redondo Beach L.A.
All over La Jolla,

(cont.)
At Wa'imea Bay.
Everybody's gone surfin',
Surfin' U.S.A.

Instrumental ‖:A | A | D | D :‖

| G | G | D | D |

Outro
Everybody's gone surfin', Surfin' U.S.A. *(Repeat to fade)*

Rock 'n' Roll Riff

The guitar on the original recording has more of a barre chord sound, with similar strumming as described above, but when we hit the chorus it goes into a rock 'n' roll pattern which requires a bit of little finger stretching.

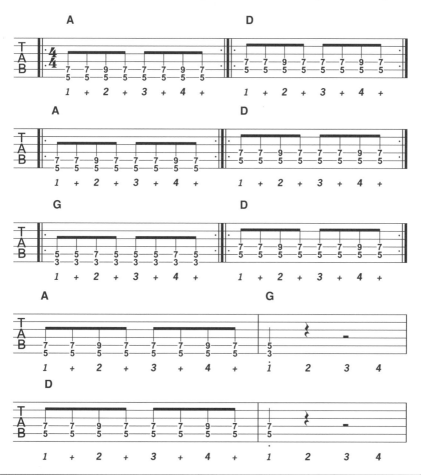

Take It Easy

Words & Music by Jackson Browne & Glenn Frey

Beginner

Intermediate

Intermediate +

TAB

Intro   ‖: G | G | C | D⁷sus⁴ :‖ G | G |

Verse 1

        G   **G**
Well I'm a-runnin' down the road tryin' to loosen my load,

      G   **D**   **C**
I've got seven women on my mind.

G   **D**
Four that wanna own me, two that wanna stone me,

C   **G**
One says she's a friend of mine.

Chorus 1

      Em Em   **C** **G**
Take it ea - sy, take it ea - sy,

          Am   **C**   **Em Em**
Don't let the sound of your own wheels drive you crazy.

     C   **G**   **C**   **G**
Lighten up while you still can, don't even try to understand,

      Am   **C**   **G G**
Just find a place to make your stand and take it ea - sy.

Link | G | G |

Verse 2

Well I'm a-standin' on a corner in Winslow, Arizona,
And such a fine sight to see;
It's a girl, my Lord, in a flat-bed Ford,
Slowin' down to take a look at me.

Chorus 2

       Em D   **C** **G**
Come on, ba - by, don't say may - be,

     Am   **C**   **Em Em**
I gotta know if your sweet love is gonna save me.

     C   **G**   **C**   **G**
We may lose and we may win, though we will never be here a - gain,

     Am   **C**   **G G**
So open up, I'm climbin' in, so take it ea - sy.

Instrumental

G	G	G D	C
G	D	C	G
Em	D	C	G
Am	C	Em	Em D

Verse 3

        G   **G**
Well, I'm a-runnin' down the road, tryin' to loosen my load,

      G   **D**   **Am**
Got a world of trouble on my mind.

G   **D**
Lookin' for a lover who won't blow my cover,

     C   **G**
She's so hard to find.

Chorus 3   Take it easy, take it easy,
Don't let the sound of your own wheels make you crazy.
Come on, baby, don't say maybe,
I gotta know if your sweet love
Is gonna save me.

Outro   ‖: C | C | G | G   :‖ C | C |
                                                    Oh we got it

‖: G | F | C | C   :‖ Em |
   Easy...

 ## Introduction

The Eagles could take it easy after having this huge hit in 1972!

Intro

Let's start at the beginning shall we? The intro uses some nice and quite specific chord grips and rhythms which really set the song up. Unfortunately, although the rhythm starts just before the beginning of the bar, your ear will probably not hear this correctly, and will think that the rhythm starts directly on beat 1 of the bar. There are a few live videos on YouTube which will help you get the correct feel for the rhythm. There's even a video recorded in Central Park, where singer Glenn Frey helpfully does a count-in for you!

The chords are shown below as is the rhythm pattern—just pop them together!

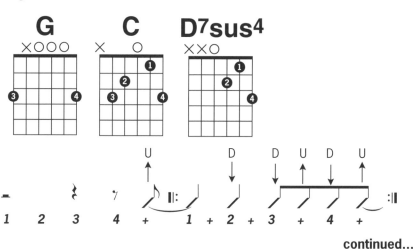

continued...

Beginner

Intermediate

Intermediate +

TAB

 Verse

Once we're into the verse of the song, the rhythm simplifies to the following basic pattern, although as there are many guitar parts and lots of variations, you can certainly experiment with other patterns too.

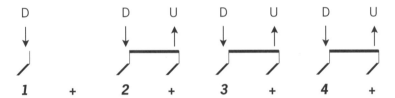

If you have a jam buddy, this will work well as a 2-guitar song: in the intro the electric guitar plays on the chord changes, while in the rest of the song, it picks notes out of the chord, one at a time. You can hear it pretty clearly on the original recording and it's loads of fun to play! If you want to improvise a solo, you should start out exploring the G Major Pentatonic scale, letting your ears guide you.

The First Cut Is The Deepest
Words & Music by Cat Stevens

Introduction

This is a wonderful song from the great Cat Stevens (now Yusuf Islam), covered by many pop singers since, including a fantastic version by Sheryl Crow.

Three Chord Trick

This is a fab three-chord song—it's easy to play, sounds great and almost everyone will know it! The song can be played using the most basic open chord shapes and a very simple rhythm pattern, as is often the case when performed by Cat / Yusuf himself these days. The only thing to watch out for is the chord sequence, which is not quite as simple as you might first think—I'll confess that when I used to play it in bands as a teenager, we used the same G D C D chord sequence all the way through and nobody ever seemed to notice! But to do it right you'll need to be aware that sometimes it alters a little, usually to G C D C.

Strumming

Several different strumming patterns will fit this song, but to keep it simple I'd start with something like the pattern below, noting that often the up-strum before a chord change (in this song usually the + after 2 and the + after 4) will briefly be strumming open strings while you change the chords, and that's fine.

 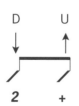 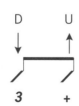 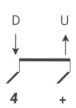

The First Cut Is The Deepest

Words & Music by Cat Stevens

Beginner
Intermediate
Intermediate +
TAB

Intro

riff ———————
|: G   D | C   D   :|

Verse 1

      | G   D | C   D
I would have given you all of my heart,
      | G   C | D   C
But there's someone who's torn it a - part,
      | G   D | C
And she's taken almost all that I've got
    D | G   D | C
But if you want I'll   try to love a - gain,
D | G   C | D   D
Baby I'll try to love a - gain, but I know

Chorus 2

| G   D | C
    The first cut is the deepest,
D | G
Baby I know,
      D | C   D
The first cut is the deepest.
      | G   D | C   D
'Cause when it comes to being lucky she's cursed,
      | G   C | D   C
When it comes to loving me she's worst,
      | G   D | C
But when it comes to being in love she's first
      D
That's how I know
| G   D | C
    The first cut is the deepest,
D | G
Baby I know,
      D | C   D | D $\frac{2}{4}$| D |
The first cut is the deepest.

Verse 2

I still want you by my side,
Just to help me dry the tears that I've cried
'Cause I'm sure gonna give you a try
And if you want I'll try to love again,
Baby I'll try to love again, but I know.

Chorus 2

As Chorus 1

Link

riff
| G   D | C   D |
                 Ba - by I know

Chorus 3

As Chorus 1   *Fade out during chorus*

🎵 Intro

I also want to give you the exact 'lead' guitar part from the record because it's really nice and not hard to play. Use a small barre with your 3rd finger for the first chord and then use the 3rd finger to slide up to the 12th fret for the next chord (D). I know it seems odd to do it that way but the slide is part of the riff's character. If it's too hard you can always leave it out. The C chord is the same as the D but down 2 frets, and then it's back to the D with the little slide. It's easy to play and sounds great! Of course you'll have to adapt the pattern to fit the chord sequence if you want to keep it going throughout the song.

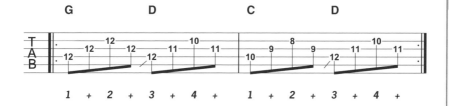

You've Got To Hide Your Love Away

Words & Music by John Lennon & Paul McCartney

Beginner

Intermediate

Intermediate +

TAB

Intro

$\frac{6}{8}$| G | G |

Verse 1

|G Dsus4 | Fadd9 C G |
Here I stand, head in hand,

C |Fadd9 C |
Turn my face to the wall.

|G Dsus4 |Fadd9 C G |
If she's gone I can't go on

|C |Fadd9 C |D
Feeling two foot small.

Verse 2

|G Dsus4 |Fadd9 C G |
Ev'rywhere peo - ple stare,

|C |Fadd9 C |
Each and ev'ry day.

|G Dsus4 |Fadd9 C G |
I can see them laugh at me,

|C |Fadd9 C |D D/C |D/B D/A |
And I hear them say:

Chorus 1

G   C |Dsus4 D |Dsus2 D |
Hey, you've got to hide your love a - way.

G   C |Dsus4 D |Dsus2 D |
Hey, you've got to hide your love a - way.

Verse 3

How can I even try?
I can never win.
Hearing them, seeing them
In the state I'm in.

Verse 4

How could she say to me
Love will find a way?
Gather round, all you clowns,
Let me hear you say:

Chorus 2

As Chorus 1

Outro

|G Dsus4 | Fadd9 C G | C | Fadd9 C |

|G Dsus4 | Fadd9 C G | C | Fadd9 C | G

Introduction

This is one of many beautiful acoustic songs by The Beatles, released in 1965 on the album *Help!*

Rhythm Guitar

There are quite specific guitar parts for this song and they are worth checking out because if you get the song right it will sound lovely. If you watch the film *Help!*, you can see John Lennon playing this song on a twelve-string guitar but it works fine on a six-string, and I believe I can hear a nylon string guitar in the mix there too.

The song is in 6/8 time—this means 2 strong pulses per bar, each of which contains 3 beats. The main rhythm of the song is played as follows, with a slight accent on the bass strings on beats 1 and 4, so as to make the pulse obvious.

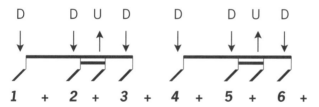

But that's not the whole picture because there are many smaller changes evident in the song, especially because there are melody elements included within the chords, for which you will need to add in strums, usually on the + after 3 and the + after 6.

One other thing to note is that in the bars with Fadd9, C and G, the C chord is held for only one beat—just beat 3!

Beginner

Intermediate

Intermediate +

TAB

49

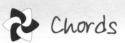

Chords

The chord grips for this song are very interesting too, and you can get a good look at them by watching the Beatles' performance in the movie, *Help!* (available on YouTube).

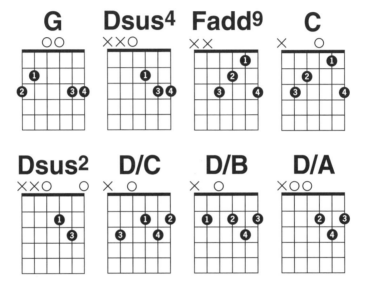

Chorus Riff

The chorus includes a melodic line, followed by a chord riff.

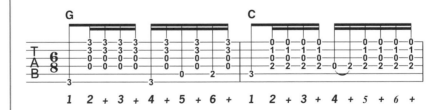

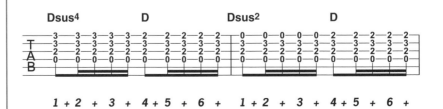

INTERMEDIATE STAGE

 ## Introduction

Now that you're not a beginner any more (congratulations, by the way!) we're going to learn some more advanced songs and skills. Above all, these Intermediate songs will help you develop your ability to play barre chords. I spent many years avoiding barre chords, and worrying that I wasn't ready, but my advice to you is to get stuck into them as soon as you are confident with all your beginner techniques.

At this stage, a big part of your studies will be learning to recognise which chords to play as barre chords, and which to play 'open'. The matter is made more interesting by the fact that many chords can be played both as open chords and as barre chords. You must decide which voicings to use in each situation. There is often no right or wrong, although there may be creative or practical reasons that lead you to choose one voicing over another.

Over the page, you will find a guide on playing the eight main barre chord shapes. When you start learning how to play barre chords, it is likely that you will find the E-shape chords (with the root on the 6th string) easiest to play, and will prefer to play them, rather than the A-shape chords. This is absolutely fine. As you get used to the A-shape barre chords, your options will increase and you will choose your voicings accordingly.

You may find that a song sounds better if all the chords are played as barre chords. At other times you will play most of the chords open, and only barre when you have to. Do what you feel most comfortable with to start with, and as your playing develops, choose the voicing that sounds best!

Also in this section I will be introducing some sixteenth-note strumming patterns. Remember that the trick to playing them is to practise them slowly and carefully and repeat them many times. 'Practice makes permanent' (not 'perfect' as is so often quoted!), and you should be aiming to practise a pattern until it feels completely natural and instinctive. A good test is to keep playing a pattern while having a conversation with someone. If you can do that then you'll have the pattern well and truly 'in the bag'.

Intermediate Stage:
Your Notes

Beginner

Intermediate

Intermediate +

TAB

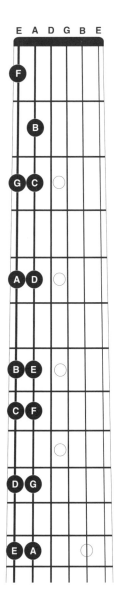

Getting Started

On the facing page are the eight essential barre chord grips. You must memorise these grips, along with the corresponding bass notes on the thickest two strings.

To find a chord, first locate the root note. If the root note is a sharp or a flat (e.g. F♯ or B♭), then move up or down one fret accordingly (sharp—move towards the bridge, flat—move towards the nut). Then use the appropriate chord shape (major, minor, 7th or minor 7th), using E-shape grips when the root note is on the 6th string, and A-shape grips when the root is on the 5th string.

If you have any problems playing any of these chords, please check out the relevant lessons in the Intermediate Method section of the web site (starting with IM-111 and IM-131).

E-Shape Barre Chords

Major **Minor** **7** **Minor 7**

   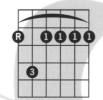

 A-Shape Barre Chords

Major **Minor** **7** **Minor 7**

 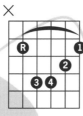 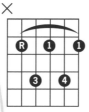 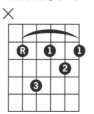

(R = Root note)

Beginner

Intermediate

Intermediate +

TAB

All I Have To Do Is Dream

Words & Music by Boudleaux Bryant

Beginner

Intermediate

Intermediate +

TAB

Intro

```
E   |E    C#m|A              B        |
     Drea - m,  dream, dream, dream,
|E    C#m|A            B
Drea - m, dream, dream, dream
```

Verse 1

```
    |E     C#m |A            B
When I want you    in my arms,
     |E     C#m |A                B
When I want you     and all your charms,
    |E     C#m    |A            B    |
Whenever I want you all I have to do is,
|E    C#m|A              B         |
Drea - m, dream, dream, dream.
```

Verse 2

```
When I feel blue in the night,
And I need you to hold me tight,
Whenever I want you all I have to do is,
|E      A    |E       E7    |
Dream. _____
```

Bridge 1

```
A
I can make you mine,
G#m
Taste your lips of wine
|F#m     B        |E      E7   |
Anytime    night or day
A              G#m
Only trouble is,    gee whiz
      F#              B
I'm dreaming my life away.
```

Verse 3

```
I need you so that I could die,
I love you so and that is why,
Whenever I want you all I have to do is
Dream, dream, dream, dream,
Dream.
```

Bridge 2

```
I can make you mine,
Taste your lips of wine
Anytime night or day
Only trouble is, gee whiz
I'm dreaming my life away.
```

Verse 4

```
I need you so that I could die,
I love you so and that is why,
Whenever I want you all I have to do is
Dream, dream, dream, dream,
Dream, dream, dream, dream.     (Repeat to fade)
```

Beginner

Intermediate

Intermediate +

TAB

Introduction

This is the Everly Brothers' beautiful ballad, recorded in 1958, which features some lovely tremolo guitar played by Chet Atkins.

Two Guitars

There are a few guitars playing on this track: at least two electrics and an acoustic. The dominant electric guitar part is played by all-time guitar legend Chet Atkins! The tremolo guitar sound at the start (most likely created by a Fender amp with a 'vibrato' effect) is one of the sweetest guitar sounds ever, and became a classic guitar sound of the 1950s and '60s.

But let's start by looking at the simpler 2nd electric guitar part. It uses all barre chords, although you can include an open E chord if you prefer—it will sound fine. There are many small variations as it goes along but for the most part the bass note of each chord is played and then followed by two strums: a down- and an up-strum. It's doubled by the piano too, so it's a little buried in the mix. The sequence for the verse is shown below, although the pattern continues for the Bridge sections as well.

E			C#m			A			B		
B	D	U	B	D	U	B	D	U	B	D	U
1	+	2	+	3	+	4	+	1	+	2	+	3	+	4	+

(B = Bass note)

continued...

Decorations

So what is Chet Atkins up to on the recording? Well, he adds some lovely decorations—some of them pretty complex. He often just strums the chords on beat 1 and 4, letting the lovely tremolo effect work its magic, although sometimes he adds in lead lines too, and there are some lovely harmonics in there too (one of his trademark techniques). Below is his simple but effective accompaniment to verse 1.

Verse 1

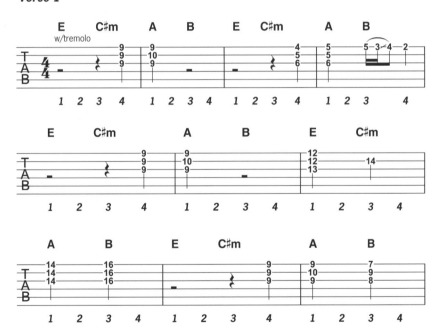

Crying
Words & Music by Roy Orbison & Joe Melson

Introduction

This song was a huge hit for the legendary singer-songwriter Roy Orbison in 1961.

Chords

There are some great videos available online that show you exactly how Roy Orbison played this song, so I will be basing this lesson on those. However, it's fine to use more conventional chord voicings instead, such as playing the D as a barre and the Daug in the more common barre chord grip shown below.

Orbison played the chords open wherever possible and often replaced the regular D with a D/F#—but don't feel you have to do this. It can sound strange when played on solo guitar—remember that Orbison could make this substitution because he had a backing band confirming the D note in the bass. The Daug is played open too, simply by adding the little finger to the D chord. It's also worth noting that for the G and G minor chords he played the bass note with his thumb, or left it off altogether, and I would recommend using the fingering as shown below because it seems to add the right flavour for this style.

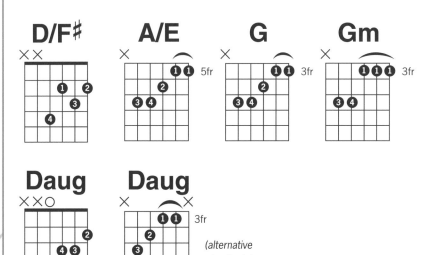

(alternative chord grip)

59

Crying

Words & Music by Roy Orbison & Joe Melson

Intro

| D | D | |

Verse 1

       D   D   D   D
I was all right for a while, I could smile for a while.
    D   Daug
But I saw you last night, you held my hand so tight
         G   N.C.   Gm
As you stopped to say hel - lo.
      D   A   A
You wished me well, you   couldn't tell   that I'd been...

Chorus 1

D   F♯m   D   F♯m
Crying over you, crying over you.
       G   A   G   A
Then you said so long, left me standing all a - lone,
            D   Daug   G   Gm
Alone and crying, crying, crying crying.
            D   D   A   A
It's hard to understand but the touch of your hand
            D   D
Can start me crying.

Verse 2

                D   D   D   D
I thought that I was over you but it's true, so true,
       D   Daug
I love you even more than I did before,
   G   N.C.   Gm
But darling what can I do?
      D   D   A/E   A/E
For you don't love me and I'll always be...

Chorus 2

D   F♯m   D   F♯m
Crying over you, crying over you.
G   A   G   A
Yes, now you're gone and from this moment on
       D   Daug   G   Gm
I'll be crying, crying, crying, crying,

Outro

        D   D   D   Bm
Yeah cry - ing, cry - ing,
G   A | D   A | D   G | D   D
O - ver you.

Strumming

The rhythm required for this tune is a little unusual but sounds great. It's a common eighth-note pattern but using all down-strums! There are many variations though, so you have to feel them out and make sure you watch out for the stops, shown as NC (No Chord) in the chord chart.

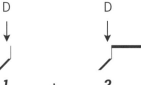
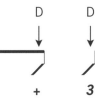
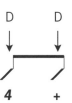

Don't Let Me Be Misunderstood

Words & Music by Bennie Benjamin, Sol Marcus & Gloria Caldwell

Beginner

Intermediate

Intermediate +

TAB

Intro

riff ———————
‖: Bm | Em :‖

Verse 1

Bm   A
Baby do you under - stand me now?
G   F♯
   Sometimes I feel a little mad.

     Bm
But don't you know that no one alive

    A
Can always be an angel,
G   F♯
   When things go wrong I seem   to be bad.

Chorus 1

           D   Bm
But I'm just a soul whose in - tentions are good,
| G N.C.   G N.C. | N.C.   (Bm)
    Oh Lord,   please don't let me be misunder - stood.

Link

riff ———————
‖: Bm | Em :‖

Verse 2

Baby, sometimes I'm so carefree
With a joy that's hard to hide.
And sometimes it seems that all I have to do is worry,
And then you're bound to see my other side.

Chorus 2

           D   Bm
But I'm just a soul whose in - tentions are good,
| G N.C.   G N.C. | N.C. | Bm A |
    Oh Lord,   please don't let me be misunder - stood.

Bridge

| G   A | G   A |
    If I seem edgy, I want you to know
| G   A | D Bm |
That I ne - ver mean to take it out on you.
| G   A | G   A |
    Life has its problems, and I get my share
G   F♯
And that's one thing I never mean to do, 'cause I love you

Verse 3

Oh, oh oh oh baby, don't you know I'm human
I have thoughts like any other one.
Sometimes I find myself long regretting
Some foolish thing, some little sinful thing I've done.

Chorus 4

D   Bm
I'm just a soul whose in - tentions are good,
|G N.C.   G N.C. | N.C.   riff
    Oh Lord,   please don't let me be misunder - stood

(Repeat chorus to fade)

 ## Introduction

This song, written for Nina Simone, was a huge hit for The Animals in 1965 and has been extensively covered. As a guitarist you should check out the awesome Robben Ford version! In this tutorial we'll be looking at The Animals' recording.

 ## Different Arrangements

This song can be played a number of different ways, as you will notice if you explore some of the cover versions of the song. The Animals' version has a lot of energy and some quite unusual rhythm feels which can seem awkward, especially if you try to play along with the recording straight away—you'll probably need to listen to it a lot first.

The riff played at the start of the song is repeated various times throughout the song—it's not difficult to play the single line, but it's also not too hard to arrange for solo guitar, playing the bass note and the melody line together. Both are shown below.

Single Line

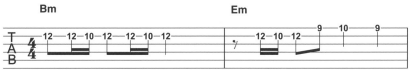

For Solo Guitar

Beginner

Intermediate

Intermediate +

TAB

 Rhythm

In the verses the guitar is playing a strange, quite choppy rhythm which is juxtaposed with the smooth ballad melody in an unexpected way. It seems that it's being played using all down-strums, with chord lifts between many of the strums. Check out the pattern below, listen closely and you'll pick it up. Personally I prefer playing this song as a ballad and either strumming a pattern like 'Old Faithful' or playing it fingerstyle.

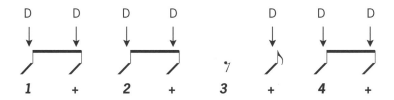

Chorus / Bridge

The chorus picks up a notch and the guitar plays all down-strums on even eighth-notes (same as the pattern above but adding the down-strum on the 3 too) but watch out for the stops on 1 and the 'and' after beat 2, which need to be tight!

The Bridge introduces a new feel again. It's more like the verse, and quite choppy, but the tricky bit here is making sure you get the chord changes in the right place—you'll have to move from the G to the A chord on the 'and' after beat 2, which can seem a little strange at first. As usual, things like this are best picked up by listening rather than thinking too hard!

I would recommend using all barre chords for this song but if you are choosing to do it fingerstyle, you might like to use open chords where you can.

It's So Easy
Words & Music by Buddy Holly & Norman Petty

 ## Introduction

Buddy Holly certainly knew how to write a catchy rock 'n' roll song and this single from 1958 is one of his finest.

 ## Rhythm

The rhythm guitar in this song is buried in the mix a bit, while the main guitar part is the electric guitar, which plays fills and lead lines. However, the acoustic guitar is in there—it's just hiding beneath the drums and bass!

The rhythm guitar part plays pretty continuous strumming but being so hidden, it's hard to say how consistent it is throughout the song.

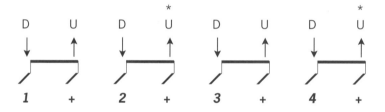

* In this sequence the up-strums that happen on the + after 2 and the + after 4 are very likely to be open strings if you are changing chords. Don't consciously try to play open strings, but it's unlikely that you'll make the chord change fast enough, and will hit them inadvertently. That is OK—it will sound authentic and nobody will notice! Obviously, you should only get these extra open strings ringing out when there are chord changes and not if you are playing one chord for a few bars!

It's So Easy
Words & Music by Buddy Holly & Norman Petty

Beginner

Intermediate

Intermediate +

TAB

Chorus 1

|A   E |D   E |
It's so easy to fall in love.
|A   D |E   A |
It's so easy to fall in love.

Instr.

| A E |D E |A D |E A |

Verse 1

|A   E |D   E
People tell me love's for fools,
   |A   D |E   A
So, here I go breakin' all o' the rules.

Bridge 1

           D   D
It seems so easy. *(Seems so easy, seems so easy.)*
           A   A
Oh, so dog-gone easy. *(Dog-gone easy, dog-gone easy.)*
           D
Mmm, it seems so easy.
                D
(Seems so easy, seems so easy, seems so easy.)
    B7   E
Where you're concerned my heart has learned…

Chorus 2

As Chorus 1

Instr.

| A E |D E |A D |E A |

Guitar solo

| D |D |A |A7 |
| D |D |B7 |E |

Chorus 3

As Chorus 1

Verse 2

Look into your heart and see
What your love-book has set apart for me.

Bridge 2

As Bridge 1

Chorus 4

As Chorus 1

Instr.

| A E |D E |A D |E A |

Bridge 3

As Bridge 1

Chorus 5

|A   E |D   E |
It's so easy to fall in love.
|A   D |E   A9 |
It's so easy to fall in love.

Solo

The solo is a true classic of its time and quite a fun one for beginners, so I've tabbed it out here for you. The first chunk is the same as the intro too!

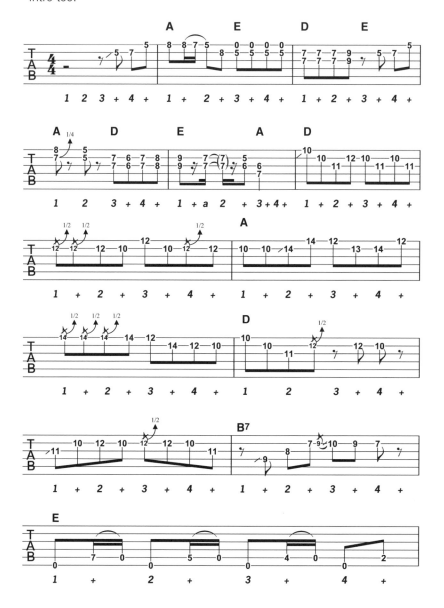

Beginner

Intermediate

Intermediate +

TAB

67

I Feel Fine

Words & Music by John Lennon & Paul McCartney

Intro

riff

| (D7) | (D7) | (C7) | (C7) |
| (G7) | (G7) | (G7) | (G7) |

Verse 1

G7   G7
Baby's good to me, you know,
    G7   G7
She's happy as can be, you know
       D7   D7
She said so.
D7   C7   G7   G7
I'm in love with her and I feel fine.

Verse 2

Baby says she's mine, you know,
She tells me all the time, you know
She said so.
I'm in love with her and I feel fine.

Bridge 1

G   Bm
I'm so glad
      C   D7
That she's my little girl,
G   Bm
She's so glad,
     Am   D7
She's telling all the world;

Verse 3

That her baby buys her things, you know,
He buys her diamond rings, you know
She said so.
She's in love with me and I feel fine.

Solo

| G7 | G7 | G7 | G7 | D7 | D7 | |

Link

As Intro

Verse 4

As Verse 2

Bridge 2

As Bridge 1

Verse 5

As Verse 3

Coda

D7   C7   G7
She's in love with me and I feel fine.

‖: G7 | G7 | G7 | G7 :‖ *(Repeat to fade)*

Beginner

Introduction

This is a great, high energy hit from The Beatles with a cracking riff to learn!

Intro

The intro riff to this song is very well known, but it can be a little tricky to play—it requires both a solid barre chord and impressive little finger dexterity! It's based on a D7, played as an E-Shape barre chord grip, but then requires some tricksy movements with your little finger (which is doing most of the work) and some intricate picking. It requires a lot of stretching too, but with some slow, careful practice I'm sure you'll nail it.

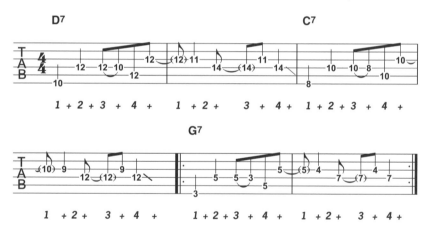

Intermediate

Intermediate +

TAB

Verse

The verses are a mixture of the riff and some strumming too. If you are singing and struggling to play the riff at the same time, you can just strum along, or play the riff and then just strum for the last D7 to C7 bit. If you are playing full chords then you should probably stick with the Root 6 barre chords for the authentic sound even though it's easier to play them further down the neck.

continued...

 Bridge

In the Bridge there are two parts, one doing fairly straight 'Old Faithful' style strumming (shown below) and the other part, which is picking out some individual notes while strumming. It's quite random and different every time: it basically just involves strumming, while allowing some notes to be accented as part of the groove. I touch on it in my Picked Fingerstyle lessons in the Intermediate Method (IM-156), but it requires experimentation!

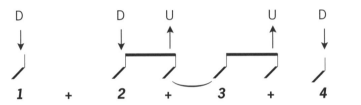

Solo

The short lead guitar solo section is quite easy—just a couple of licks before joining the riff. Make sure you listen to the original to pick up the right vibe for the slides and the lazy groove.

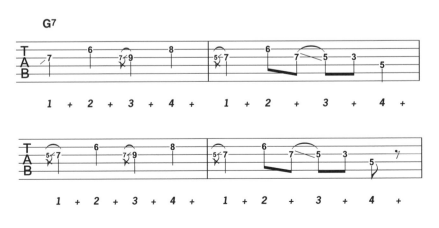

In My Life

Words & Music by John Lennon & Paul McCartney

Introduction

This is another wonderful track by The Beatles, this time from the legendary album *Rubber Soul* (1965).

Intro Riff

Let's start with the intro riff, which appears at various points in the song. It's an all-time classic, and you can add low open bass notes to it as well if you are playing on your own. Try to let the notes ring out together to make it sound authentic.

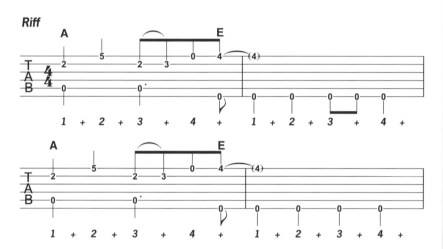

Strumming

The rhythm playing is quite crude, mostly with down-strums hitting the bass strings but you should place the whole chord down nonetheless. I've written out a kind of sample of it, but it varies a lot throughout the song; sometimes it follows the vocal rhythms and sometimes it just plods along in a very restrained way. Watch out for the spots where the chord is played just once and held, as well as the dynamic shifts, which are very important in this song.

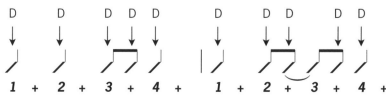

In My Life

Words & Music by John Lennon & Paul McCartney

Beginner

Intermediate

Intermediate +

TAB

Intro

riff
```
‖: A      | E        :‖
```

Verse 1

```
        | A      E    |F♯m    A7/G
There are places I re - member
        | D    Dm      | A
All my life,___ though some have changed,
        | A      E    |F♯m    A7/G
Some forever, not for better,
        | D      Dm    | A
Some have gone___ and some remain.
```

Bridge 1

```
        F♯m                 D
All these places had their moments,
     G                   A
With lovers and friends I still can recall,
        F♯m             B
Some are dead and some are living,
   Dm7          A
In my life I've loved them all.
```

Link

Play **riff**

Verse 2

But of all these friends and lovers,
There is no-one compares with you,
And these memories lose their meaning
When I think of love as something new.

Bridge 2

Though I know I'll never lose affection
For people and things that went before,
I know I'll often stop and think about them,
In my life I love you more.

Solo

```
‖: A    E    | F♯m  A7/G | D  Dm  | A        :‖
```

Bridge 3

As Bridge 2

Coda

```
| A      | E      | Dm7      N.C.    (A)
                    In my life, I love you more.

| A      | E7     | A        |
```

Lead Guitar Rhythm Pattern

While the rhythm guitar is chugging along, the lead part uses a more delicate arpeggiated pattern, playing the bass note on the beat and then slowly strumming up the chord so it's almost an arpeggio. It sounds great but it's low in the mix and hard to hear, so you'll need to listen out for it. There are a few pushes in there, where the chord is played an eighth-note earlier than you might expect, so watch out for them too!

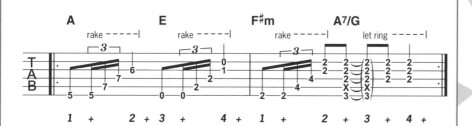

I Heard It Through The Grapevine

Words & Music by Norman J. Whitfield & Barrett Strong

Capo Fret **1**

Beginner

Intermediate

Intermediate +

TAB

Intro

riff 1

‖:Dm   :‖   *Play x6*

riff 2

‖:Dm G/D Dm │ Dm G/D :‖

Verse 1

     │Dm   G/D   Dm │
Ooh, I bet you're wondering how I knew
│Dm G/D Dm │A⁷   G⁷ │
   'Bout your plans to make me blue
  G⁷   │Dm   G/D   Dm│
   With some other guy you knew before,
│Dm   G/D Dm │A⁷
   Between the two of us guys
                G⁷ │ G⁷
You know I love you more.

Bridge 1

            Bm   G⁷
It took me by surprise I must say,
      D⁷   G⁷
When I found out yesterday.

Chorus 1

            │D⁷   G   D⁷ │
Don't you know that I heard it through the grapevine,
D⁷   G⁷   G⁷
  Not much longer would you be mine.
    │D⁷   G   D⁷ │
Oh, I heard it through the grapevine,
D⁷   G⁷   G⁷
  Oh, and I'm just about to lose my mind.
            Dm **(w/riff 1)**
Honey, honey, yeah. (*Heard it through the grapevine,*
        Dm   Dm   Dm
Not much longer would you be my baby, oooh.)

Verse 2

I know a man ain't supposed to cry
But these tears I can't hold inside.
Losin' you would end my life you see,
'Cause you mean that much to me.

Bridge 2

You could have told me yourself
That you love someone else.

Chorus 2

As Chorus 1

Link

‖:Dm G/D Dm │ Dm G/D :‖

74

Verse 3	People say believe half of what you see, Son, and none of what you hear. But I can't help bein' confused If it's true please tell me dear.
Bridge 3	Do you plan to let me go For the other guy you loved before?
Chorus 3	As Chorus 1
Outro	(cont. riff 1)　　Dm　Dm ‖: Honey, honey I know
	Dm　Dm That you're letting me go. :‖ *Repeat to fade with vocal ad lib.*

Introduction

This is Marvin Gaye's Motown hit from 1968.

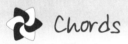

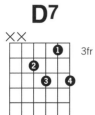

Chords

The main guitar part on the original recording is played using barre chords and 'chips'—these are very tight guitar strums on beats 2 and 4. You must have the shape of the chord prepared and then strum and press the chord down but only for an instant—the chord shouldn't ring out for long. You'll hear it clearly on the recording, now that I've mentioned it.

There are quite a few interesting things going on, one of the hardest of which is the change of chord on beat 4 in the verses—the first time it happens is on the word 'blue' on the second line. This change to the G7 chord happens on beat 4, which is very unusual but sounds natural once you've done it a few times and become used to it.

The change to D Major for the chorus can sound a bit strange at first too, but it works well once you get used to it. It's funny how things are sometimes different to what you expect, even when you've heard a song many, many times! For the D7 you will probably want to use this grip, which gives you all the thin strings you want for the 'chips'.

D7

×× ❶ 3fr
❷
❸ ❹

continued...

Riffs

The main riff is played by an organ, but below I have written out an arrangement of it for guitar. You can use it for the verses, although it might require a little experimenting!

Riff 1

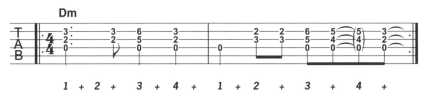

The chords that appear during the intro (marked Riff 2) are played like this—they will work well played alongside the main organ riff if you are playing in a band, although if you're playing solo, you will probably want to check out the organ riff arrangement.

Riff 2

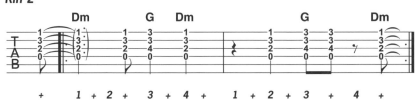

There's also a cool little guitar riff on the 'honey, honey yeah' line which will take a little practice to transition in and out of but will sound great.

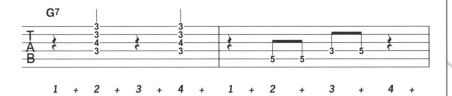

I Shot The Sheriff
Words & Music by Bob Marley

Introduction

Recorded in Kingston, Jamaica, this is the original Bob Marley version of the reggae classic, released on The Wailers' album *Burnin'* (1973). Bear in mind that if you want to play the Eric Clapton version, you'll have to transpose up one semitone.

Rhythm

The recording of this song has a lot of complex parts, intricate rhythms that change throughout the song, wah-wah single lines and muted hits. It would be impossible to go into depth in this book about each and every part but I'll give you enough bones that you can flesh it out yourself by listening and imitating the original recording.

The chords are not particularly hard, but the rhythms in reggae are complex and a lot of fun! The chorus rhythm (it starts with a chorus) is pretty hardcore, and you will absolutely have to listen to it a bunch of times to get it right.

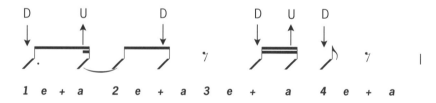

Once we hit the verses we're playing a little less, but as the song progresses there are quite a few embellishments that you can add in once you get more confident with the basic groove. Remember to keep the notes nice and short, tight and locked in with the drums and bass. It has to feel nice, relaxed and 'in the pocket'.

Dmaj7   **C#m7**

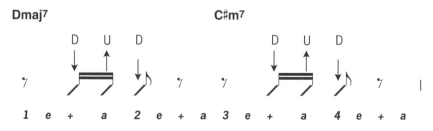

I Shot The Sheriff

Words & Music by Bob Marley

Beginner
Intermediate
Intermediate +
TAB

Chorus 1

F♯m   Bm⁷   F♯m   F♯m
I shot the sheriff,   but I did not shoot the deputy.

F♯m   Bm⁷   F♯m   F♯m
I shot the sheriff,   but I did not shoot the deputy.

Verse 1

|Dmaj⁷   C♯m⁷ |F♯m
All   around in my home town

|Dmaj⁷   C♯m⁷ |F♯m
They're trying to track me down.

    |Dmaj⁷   C♯m⁷ |F♯m
They say they want to bring me in guilty,

     |Dmaj⁷   C♯m⁷ |F♯m
For the killing of a depu - ty,

      |Dmaj⁷   C♯m⁷ |F♯m   riff
For the life of a depu - ty, but I say:

Chorus 2

I shot the sheriff, but I swear it was in self-defence.
I shot the sheriff, and they say it is a capital offence.

Verse 2

Sheriff John Brown always hated me,
For what I don't know.
Every time that I plant a seed,
He said, 'Kill it before it grows,'
He said, 'Kill them before they grow,' I say:

Chorus 3

As Chorus 2

Verse 3

Freedom came my way one day,
And I started out of town, yeah.
All of a sudden I see Sheriff John Brown,
Aimin' to shoot me down.
So I shot, I shot him down, and I say: riff (F♯m)

Chorus 4

As Chorus 1

Verse 4

Reflexes got the better of me
And what is to be must be.
Everyday the bucket a-go a well,
But one day the bottom a-go drop out,
Yes, one day the bottom a-go drop out. I say:

Chorus 5

As Chorus 1   *(Repeat ad lib. to fade)*

Beginner

Intermediate

Intermediate +

TAB

 Riff

This song would not be complete without the main riff, of course!
Luckily it's easy compared with the rhythms, as it's just based on the
F♯ Minor Pentatonic scale.

(F♯m)

1 e + a 2 e + a 3 e + a 4 e + a   1 e + a 2   +   3 + 4 +

You might also like to play about with single lines and wah-wah. Just
experiment using chord tones or the F♯ Minor Pentatonic scale.

Love Me Tender

Words & Music by Elvis Presley & Vera Matson

Intro

$\frac{2}{4}$ | D | D |

Verse 1

D   D/A   E7   E7/B
Love me tender,   love me sweet,

A7   A7/E   D   D/A
Never let me go.

D   D/A   E7   E7/B
You have made my life complete

A7   A7/E   D   D/A
And I love you so.

Chorus 1

D   F#7/C#   Bm   D7/A
Love me tender, love me true,

G   Gm6   D   D/A
All my dreams fulfilled.

D   B7   E7   E7/B
For my darling I love you

A7   A7/E   D   D/A
And I always will.

Verse 2

Love me tender, love me long,
Take me to your heart.
For it's there that I belong
And will never part.

Chorus 2

As Chorus 1

Verse 3

Love me tender, love me dear,
Tell me you are mine.
I'll be yours through all the years
Till the end of time.

Chorus 3

As Chorus 1

Beginner

Intermediate

Intermediate +

TAB

 # Introduction

Long live The King! Elvis Presley's beautiful ballad (based on an American civil war song) was recorded in 1956, without his usual guitarist Scotty Moore.

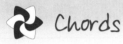 # Chords

This is a perfect example of a country ballad: nylon string guitar played gently; 2/4 time (two beats in a bar); bass notes on beat 1 and a strum on beat 2. It's simple but effective! To keep things clear we've written in the bass notes for you but don't let it scare you, it's just the bass note you should play—D/A is just a D chord but with an additional open A bass note! It mainly uses easy open chord shapes but there are a couple of tricky chords that push it past beginner level. Those chords are:

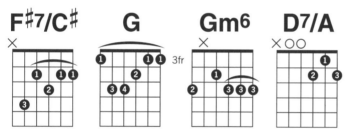

 # Rhythm

The rhythm is really simple. Play the bass note on beat 1, but put the whole chord down anyway, in case you hit other strings by mistake (then it won't matter as all the strings will be playing chord notes). Then strum the chord—not too fast—so you can almost hear each note and let them ring. The best way to learn this is to get the technique down and then listen to the record and really try to make your guitar sound just like it.

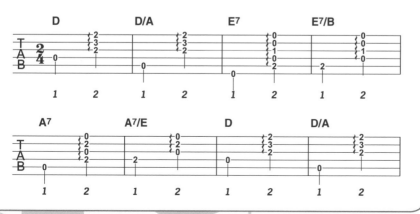

Sweet Caroline

Words & Music by Neil Diamond

Capo Fret **2**

Beginner

Intermediate

Intermediate +

TAB

Intro

‖: **E5** :‖ *Play x8*

Verse 1

A   A
Where it be - gan,
D   D
I can't be - gin to know when,
A   A   E   E
But then I know it's growing strong.
A   A
Was in the spring,
D   D
And spring be - came the summer.
A   A   E   E
Who'd have be - lieved you'd come a - long?

Pre-chorus 1

A   A A6   A6 E   E
Hands,   touching hands,   reaching out,
D   D   E   E
   Touching me, touching you.

Chorus 1

A   D
Sweet Caro - line,
D   D   E   E
  Good times never seem so good.
A   D   D |E
I've been in - clined   to believe they never would.
D |C#m Bm |
But now I...

Verse 2

Look at the night,
And it don't seem so lonely,
We fill it up with only two.
And when I hurt,
Hurting runs off my shoulders.
How can I hurt when holding you?

Pre-chorus 2

One, touching one, reaching out
Touching me, touching you.

Chorus 2

As Chorus 1

Link

As Intro

Chorus 3

Sweet Caroline,
Good times never seem so good.
Sweet Caroline,
I believe they never could.

(Repeat to fade)

Introduction

Good times never seemed so good for Neil Diamond back in 1969.

Intro / Verse

This song is most commonly played using regular open chords and with just a few barre chords coming in at the end of the chorus. But there are some cool things we can add in to make the guitar part more interesting. The intro part can be arranged nicely for solo guitar, creating a great workout for your picking hand! You'll need to keep a steady bass part with the thumb while picking out the melody line with your fingers. It'll sound awesome as an intro.

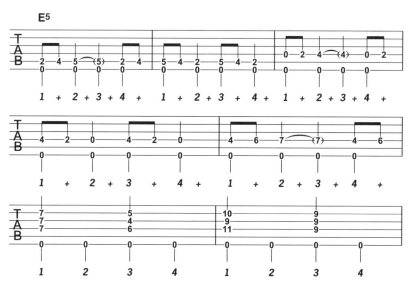

You can carry the idea through the verses too if you wish, putting chord stabs on beats 1 and 2 and bass notes for the rest of the chord:

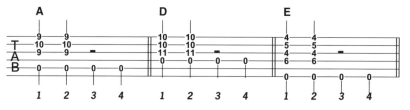

But saying that, you should still work on strumming your way through and keeping it simple—much as Neil Diamond himself, when he plays it on acoustic guitar, keeping the rhythm simple and playing mostly down-beats with some ups added in, such as fills going into choruses.

Suspicious Minds

Words & Music by Mark James

Beginner

Intermediate

Intermediate +

TAB

Intro

riff 1 ─────────

| G   C/G | G   C/G |

Verse 1

w/riff 1

|G   C/G |G   C/G |
  We're caught in a trap,

riff 2 ─────────

|C   F/C |C   F/C |
  I can't walk out

D   C |G   C/G| G   C/G |
  Because I love you too much baby.

|G   C/G |G   C/G |
  Why can't you see

|C   F/C |C   F/C|
  What you're doing to me,

D   C |D   C| Bm   D |
  When you don't believe a word I'm saying?

Chorus 1

C   G   Bm |C   D |
  We can't go on together   with suspicious minds

Em   Bm   C   D
  And we can't build our dreams   on suspicious minds.

Verse 2

So if an old friend I know
Stops by to say hello
Would I still see suspicion in your eyes?
Here we go again
Asking where I've been,
You can't see the tears are real I'm crying.

Chorus 2

C   G   Bm |C   D |
We can't go on together   with suspicious minds

Em   Bm   C |B⁷sus⁴   B⁷ |
And we can't build our dreams   on suspicious minds.

Bridge

$\frac{6}{8}$ Em   Bm   C   D
  Oh let our love survive, I'll dry the tears from your eyes

Em   Bm
Let's don't let a good thing die

C   D   G   C
  When honey, you know I've never lied to you, hmmm-mmm,

G $\frac{4}{4}$ D
Yeah, yeah.

Verse 3

We're caught in a trap,
I can't walk out
Because I love you too much baby.
Why can't you see
What you're doing to me,
When you don't believe a word I'm saying.
Ah don't you know...

Beginner
Intermediate
Intermediate +
TAB

Verse 4   𝄆 As Verse 3 𝄇   *Repeat to fade*

Introduction
This was a huge hit for The King, Elvis Presley, in 1969. It was Elvis's comeback hit and 17th US No.1!

Rhythm

This song has a really cool guitar riff but I'd suggest first that you learn the song by strumming through the chords. It's got a nice mix of open chords and barre chords, but you can play it as all barre chords too—either will work. I'd recommend starting with a very simple strumming pattern and getting to grips with the chords—you should be able to strum along with the original recording before including any of the fancy riffs.

D   D   D   U   D

1   +   2   +   3   +   4   +

Chords

Although the C/G and F/C chords are integral to the riffs, these can also be played using open chords, as shown below:

  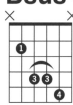

C/G   F/C   Bsus4

85

Beginner

Intermediate

Intermediate +

TAB

 Bridge

Watch out for the Bridge section, which changes time signature from 4/4 to 6/8. Rather than trying to explain the theory, I think you'll have more luck just listening to the original recording—it makes a lot more sense musically than it does theoretically. For the 6/8 section you'll be strumming just twice in each bar, on the 1 and the 4 if you are counting, but again it's easier to work out by listening to the recording than by painstakingly counting along!

 Riff

To play the riff you'll be picking out notes from the chords and adding some extra embellishment notes. The rhythm is tricky too so it's worth counting that out a few times and getting to grips with it before starting on the notes! Below is the general pattern for every G to C/G chord change (Riff 1) and the general pattern for every C to F/C sequence (Riff 2)

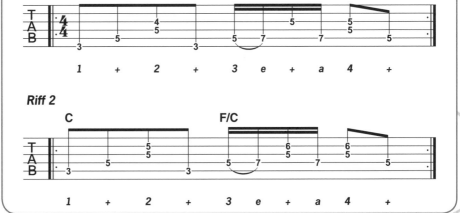

The Weight
Words & Music by Robbie Robertson

Introduction

The Band—the name says it all! This song was released by Bob Dylan's frequent collaborators on their debut album, but we're looking at the later live version recorded for *The Last Waltz* concert and album. It's worth mentioning that the *Last Waltz* version is tuned up a semitone—whether this was intentional or a result of the tape being sped up is open for debate!

Rhythm

This is an incredible song. The Band's studio albums are amazing, and if you haven't seen the movie *The Last Waltz*, documenting The Band's farewell concert in San Francisco, then do so now! As well as being artists and writers in their own right, The Band were Bob Dylan's backing band for some time, and also worked with Neil Young, Joni Mitchell and several other stars of the era, who all came by for *The Last Waltz* concert.

This song can be played in several different ways and there are often a few guitars playing simultaneously, giving you have a number of different options. The first approach is to create an acoustic vibe, where you would play as many of the chords as you can using open grips—to make it easier you could use a capo on fret 2 (all of the chord shapes will now be down one tone, so an A chord will be played as a G), but if you choose to play it without a capo, remember that you can always leave out the 'slash' chords. The letter after the slash just indicates the bass note and it's not vitally important if you are only strumming along. The rhythm will vary a lot but as a starting point you might try something like:

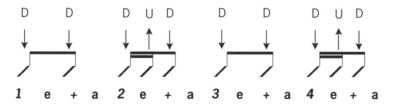

There are some tricky rhythms to recreate in this song, the hardest being the stop in the chorus with the cool vocal harmonies. It's just a 3/4 bar but the phrasing makes it sound more complicated—the trick here is to count along several times until you can 'feel' it, and have the rhythm internalised. The guitar is silent during this section so the challenge is just coming in at the right time!

The Weight

Words & Music by Robbie Robertson

Beginner

Intermediate

Intermediate +

TAB

Intro

Play Intro **riff**

| A | A | |

Verse 1

|A   C#m |D   A |
I pulled into Nazareth, just feelin' 'bout half past dead
|A   C#m |D   A |
I just need to find a place where I can lay my head
|A   C#m |D   A |
'Hey, mister, can you tell me where a man might find a bed?'
|A   C#m |D   A |
He just grinned and shook my hand and 'No' was all he said.

Chorus 1

|A   E/G# D |
Take a load off Fanny
|A   E/G# D |
Take a load for free
|A   E/G# D |
Take a load off Fanny
D 2   3   4 $\frac{3}{4}$D   2   3 $\frac{4}{4}$(A)
And (*and*) (*and*) you put the load right on me.

Link 1

| A | D | |

Verse 2

I picked up my bag, I went lookin' for a place to hide
When I saw old Carmen and the Devil walkin' side by side
I said, 'Hey Carmen, come on let's go downtown'
She said 'I gotta go, but my friend can stick around.'

Chorus 2

As Chorus 1

Link 2

| A | D | |

Verse 3

Go down, Miss Moses, there's nothin' you can say
It's just old Luke and Luke's waitin' on the Judgement Day
'Hey Luke, my friend, what about young Anna Lee?'
He said, 'Do me a favour, son,
Won't you stay and keep Anna Lee company?' Whoah!

Chorus 3

As Chorus 1

Link 3

| A | D | |

Verse 4

Crazy Chester followed me and he caught me in the fog
He said 'I will fix your rack if you'll take old Jack, my dog'
I said, 'Wait a minute, Chester, no, I'm a peaceful man'
He said, 'That's OK boy, won't you feed him when you can.' Oh!

Chorus 4	As Chorus 1

Link 4   ‖: A | D   :‖

Verse 5

Catch a cannon ball, now to take me down the line
My bag is sinking low and I do believe it's time
To get back to Miss Fanny, you know she's the only one
She sent me here with her regards for everyone.

Chorus 4	As Chorus 1

Outro   ‖: A | D   :‖

Rhythm (cont.)

There are numerous hits and accents to pick up as well, which are far easier to learn by listening to the song than by me trying to describe them here. It's such an organic, live feel that you really want to get the vibe more than the exact patterns, anyhow.

To play an electric part more like what Robbie Robertson (one of the greatest guitar players ever) played on *The Last Waltz* you should play all the chords as barre chords and add in small lead lines as you please, or pick out some of the notes from the chords.

E/G♯

Intro

Below is a TAB of the intro as played on *The Last Waltz*.

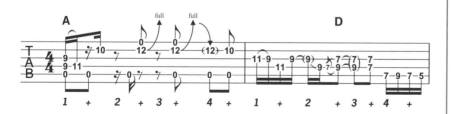

Beginner

Intermediate

Intermediate +

TAB

89

Try A Little Tenderness

Words & Music by Harry Woods, James Campbell & Reginald Connelly

Beginner

Intermediate

Intermediate +

TAB

Intro

$\frac{4}{4}$ | G | G   B⁷ | C | A   D |

Verse 1

$\frac{6}{8}$ G   Em
Ooh, she may be weary

Am   D
And young girls they do get weary

G   F   E⁷   E⁷
Wearing that same old shaggy dress,

Am   Am
But when she gets weary,

D   D   G/B   B♭ | Am | D |
Try a little tender - ness, yeah.

Verse 2

$\frac{4}{4}$ G   Em   Am   D
You know she's waiting,   just anticipating

Gmaj⁷   F⁷   E⁷   E⁷
The thing that she'll never, never, never, never, possess, yeah,

Am   Am
But while   she's there waiting

D   D   G
And without them, try a little tenderness,

C   G   G
That's all you gotta do.

Bridge

C   C   B⁷   B⁷
It's not just sentimental, no, no, no,

Em Em   A⁷   A⁷
She has her griefs and care,

C   C   B⁷   B⁷
But the soft words they are spoke so gentle, yeah,

A⁷   A⁷   C/D   D
It makes it easier,   easier to bear.

Verse 3

You won't regret it, no, no, young girls they don't forget it,
Love is their whole happiness, yeah, yeah, yeah,
But it's all so easy, all you gotta do is try...

Bridge 2

      G/B   G/B
Try a little   tenderness,   yeah.

        E⁷
Oh, you gotta   do it now,

E⁷
Hold her where you wanna.

Outro

‖: |Am   Bm |C
   Squeeze her,   don't tease her,

C♯ |D   D♯
Never leave her,   make love to her,

  |E   F   F♯ |G7
Just,   just, just try a little tenderness, yeah, yeah, yeah,

F7   E7   E7
  You've gotta know how to love her, man. :‖ *Repeat to fade*

Introduction

Otis Redding had one of the finest voices of all time and this version of a jazz standard, released in 1966, became one of his best-known recordings.

Chords

This is a very interesting song to work on, as the guitar playing on the recording is pretty sparse—but sometimes less says more. Try listening to the recording a few times before playing it and listen out for the subtle quality of the performance. It's so fragile and full of 'tenderness' but at the same time biting and harsh. It's top quality playing from Steve Cropper, the Stax Records resident guitarist.

Even though many of these chords can be played open (which is well worth trying out), to create a similar vibe to the recording you should use mostly barre chords. Note that an E7 in this style is shown below. Most of the other 7th chords you'll be playing are the Root 6 type, also shown below so you don't have to look them up! I've also added a nice grip for the C/D but I'm hoping you know or can easily figure out the remaining barre chords—if not you might like to go check out the relevant Intermediate Method lessons on the website!

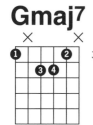
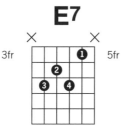
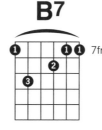
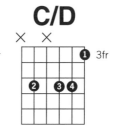

Rhythm, etc.

There is no need for a strumming pattern—just strum on the chord changes and then add some light strums or pick out notes between. More advanced players might like to try adding in some fills, but don't go spoiling it by making it too busy!

The Commitments did an amazing cover of this song (for the film *The Commitments*), which is well worth looking up. Their version is in the key of E so you'll need to move every chord down by 3 semitones—transposing (changing key) is a very useful skill and this is a great song to try it out with. It's a lot easier than it might first appear, particularly when you're using barre chords.

Unchained Melody

Words by Hy Zaret, Music by Alex North

Introduction

The song was a huge hit for The Righteous Brothers in 1965, although incredibly it had been released several times by different artists in the preceding 10 years! As with 'Be My Baby', this recording benefits from the epic production of Phil Spector.

Chips n' Barres

What a huge song, and what a voice! The recording contains no auto-tuning or tweaking, just the raw talent of Bobby Hatfield (one of the Righteous Brothers) giving it everything. It's easy to forget what an incredible recording this is—what a performance! And you can tell that the band were playing together live, all in one room, making real music.

The guitar part in this song plays 'chips' on beats 2 and 4. If you are not sure about playing 'chips', you should check out the lesson on my website (IM-155) for a detailed look at them. The basic concept is that you play the chords short and tight on the 2nd and 4th strong beats of each bar. You'll hear these 'chips' on the recording if you listen out for them. Remember that this song is in 12/8, which is 4 strong beats divided into 3 pulses each.

You should use barre chords all the way through as they are easier to keep tight and under control.

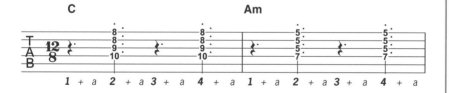

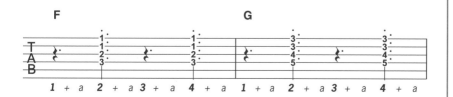

Unchained Melody

Words by Hy Zaret, Music by Alex North

Beginner

Intermediate

Intermediate +

TAB

Verse 1

$\frac{12}{8}$ C   Am   F
Oh, my＿ love, my darling,

      G   C
I've hungered for your touch

    Am   G G
A long, lonely time.

        C   Am   F
And time goes＿ by so slowly,

      G   C
And time can do so much,

      Am   G
Are＿ you still mine?

G C   G
I   need your love,

Am   Em
I need your love,

       F   G C   C7
God - speed your love to me.

Bridge

|F   G |F   E♭ |
Lonely rivers flow to the sea, to the sea,

|F   G |C
To the open arms of the sea, yeah.

|F   G |F   E♭ |
Lonely rivers sigh, wait for me, wait for me,

|F   G |C
I'll be coming home, wait for me.

Verse 2

Oh, my love, my darling,
I've hungered, hungered for your touch
A long, lonely time.
And time goes by so slowly,
And time can do so much,
Are you still mine?
I need your love, I, I need your love,

       F   G (C)
Godspeed your love to me.

Outro
*Slowing
down*

|C |Am |F Fm |C |

Fingerstyle Pattern

Very often you will hear people playing a fingerstyle arrangement of this song that to some extent mimics the electric piano part on the recording. As the song is in 12/8 you will want to play the bass note on beat 1, and probably on beat 3 (the 3rd strong beat) and fill the remaining pulses with random notes from the chords. 'Random notes from the chords' is often harder to do than to say, so I'd suggest starting out with a set fingerstyle pattern like something shown below and then experiment, knowing that really as long as you keep the bass note on beat 1 you can play whatever you like! Let your ears be your guide.

You'll notice that here we're using open chords, rather than the barre chords that we used for the 'chips'.

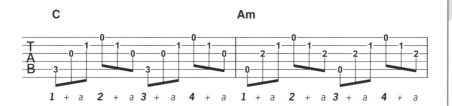

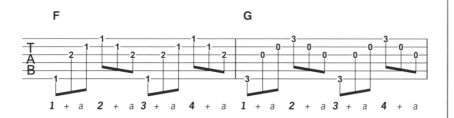

Angie

Words & Music by Mick Jagger & Keith Richards

Intro | Am Am7 Am | E7 E7/G♯ | Gsus4 Fsus4 F | F Csus4 C Gsus4/B |

Verse 1

Am   E7
 Angie,   Angie,
|G Gsus4   G   Fsus4 F |C Csus4 C Gsus4/B |
    When will those clouds all disappear?

Am   E7
 Angie,   Angie,
|G Gsus4   G Fsus4 F |Csus4 C |
    Where will it lead   us from here?

Chorus 1

         G
With no lovin' in our souls
    |Dm   Am |
And no money in our coats,
|C   F |G
    You can't say we're satisfied.
Am   E7
Angie,   Angie,
|G Gsus4 G   Fsus4 F |Csus4 Csus2 C Gsus4/B |
    You   can't say   we nev - er tried.

Verse 2

Angie, you're beautiful, yeah,
But ain't it time we said goodbye?
Angie, I still love you,
Remember all those nights we cried.

Chorus 2

All the dreams we held so close
Seemed to all go up in smoke.
Let me whisper in your ear,
'Angie, Angie,
Where will it lead us from here?'

Instrumental | Am | E7 | Gsus4 G Gsus4 G Fsus4 F Fsus2 F |

| Csus4 C Csus2 C Gsus4/B | Am | E7 |

| Gsus4 G Fsus4 F | Csus4 C Csus2 C Gsus4/B |

Chorus 3

Oh, Angie don't you weep,
All your kisses, they'll taste sweet,
I hate that sadness in your eyes.
But Angie, Angie,
Ain't it time we said goodbye?

Instrumental	│ Am │ E7 │ G Gsus4 G Fsus4 F Fsus2 F │

│ Csus4 C Csus2 C │

Chorus 4
With no lovin' in our souls
And no money in our coats,
You can't say we're satisfied.

Bridge

    Dm   **Am**
But Angie, I still love you baby,

Dm   **Am**
   Everywhere I look I see your eyes.

Dm   **Am**
   There ain't a woman that comes close to you,

│**C**   **F**   │**G**
   Come on baby dry your eyes.

Verse 3
Angie, Angie,
Ain't it good to be alive?
Angie, Angie,
They can't say we never tried.

Introduction

This song was a huge hit for The Rolling Stones in 1973 and includes one of the finest acoustic guitar parts ever written!

Strumming

The strumming requires very loose sixteenth-note playing, meaning that it would be quite a task to write the whole thing out. If you really want to nail it then you should start with this simplified pattern shown below and listen to the song over and over until you gradually absorb the rhythm. You'll notice that the chorus in particular adds in more sixteenth-note strums.

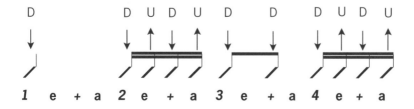

Chords

This is a great song for acoustic guitar, with some fun, sophisticated chords in it— although you can always simplify them if you need to.

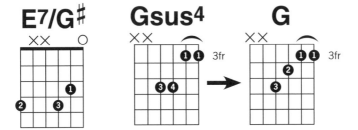

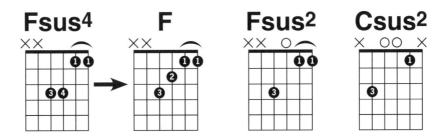

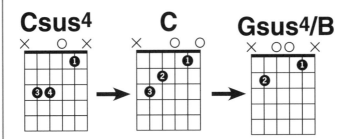

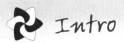

Intro

It's said that Keith Richards spent a whole week practising and perfecting the 'Angie' intro—I have no idea if that's true or not, but it certainly sounds amazing and it's remarkably difficult to perfect it. However, putting time into the intro will certainly improve your sense of time and make the rest of the song seem comparatively easy! It's the rhythms that are most challenging, so as usual, play along with the original recording at a slower speed is—that's how I learned it!

Intro

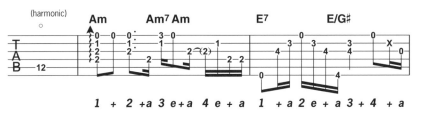

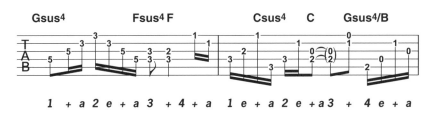

Verse 1

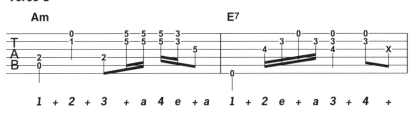

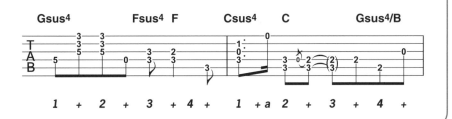

Beginner — Intermediate — Intermediate + — TAB

Beginner

Intermediate

Intermediate +

TAB

 ## Introduction

Now we're going to make things a little more interesting!

It's good to keep learning new techniques and ideas, and fortunately there is a wealth of riffs and songs out there to keep you inspired. In this exciting selection, we look at songs that feature riffs, licks, unusual time signatures, interesting chord grips, fingerstyle patterns and a whole lot more.

With any of the more complex songs, the key to learning them well is to practise them really slowly at first. When I teach private lessons I see—time and time again—students attempting to play songs too fast, too early on in their practice. See the 'Practice Tips' at the front of this book for a structured guide on practising more advanced material.

Beginner

Intermediate

Intermediate +

TAB

Intermediate + Stage:
Your Notes

Green Onions

Music by Steve Cropper, Booker T. Jones, Al Jackson & Lewie Steinberg

Intro ‖: F5   (A♭)   (B♭) | F5   (A♭)   (B♭) :‖   *(no guitar)*

(Riff 1)

Tune ‖: F | F | F | F |

| B♭ | B♭ | B♭ | B♭ |

| F | F | F | F |

| C | B♭ | F | F   :‖

Organ solo ‖: (Riff 2) :‖

Guitar solo ‖: See solo :‖

Organ solo 2 ‖: (Riff 2) :‖

Outro ‖: F5   (A♭)   (B♭) | F5   (A♭)   (B♭) :‖   *(Repeat to fade, guitar ad lib.)*

Introduction

This is an all-time guitar classic from Booker T. & the M.G.'s, featuring the legendary session guitar player (and bandmember) Steve Cropper.

The Riffs

This song is made up of several riffs, none of which are complex so it's the rhythm that becomes the most important feature—locking into the groove and getting the guitar part 'in the pocket' is essential. It is basically a 12-bar blues pattern, so most of the riff 'shapes' will follow the chords (but note the 4-bar organ introduction before the chord sequence starts).

Riff 1 is a simple 'chip' (short staccato note) that comes on the 'and' after beat 4 of each bar. It's an unusual choice of notes too but it sounds awesome. I've divided the riff into the three different components—each time you seen an F, B♭ or C chord on the songsheet, play the relevant riff below, remembering to start the riff just a half beat before the chord change.

Riff 1

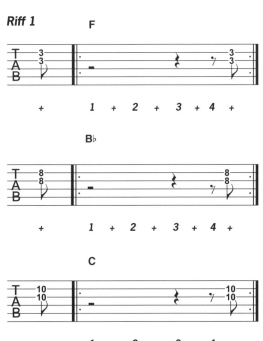

Beginner

Intermediate

Intermediate +

TAB

Riff 2

Riff 2 doubles the bass guitar and is played twice through while the organ plays the melody. It's a simple riff to play but again, make sure you lock in with the rhythm section (bass and drums) and keep it tight. Listen closely to the original recording so you can hear the 'skip' in the rhythm, and the way that all the instruments sit together to create a great groove. Again, this riff has been broken down into the three different components, to be played over the three different chords (F, B♭ and C).

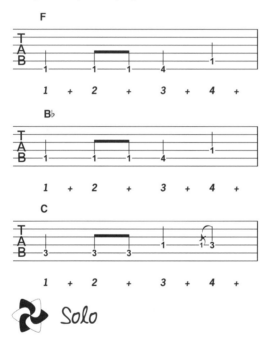

Solo

The guitar solo begins at 1:10. It starts with what sounds like an improvised solo, although the second time through the sequence, the guitar settles on a repeated melody which shifts up and down with the chord changes. You'll also hear a reverb effect kick in on the guitar at this point. After the solo, we're back to playing Riff 2 while the organ takes a solo, again playing twice through the sequence. After the organ solo we have a very short guitar solo section and then the song fades out.

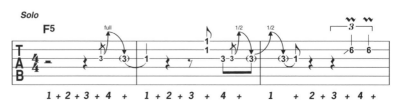

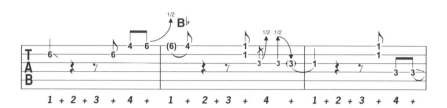

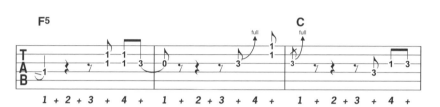

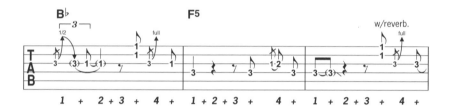

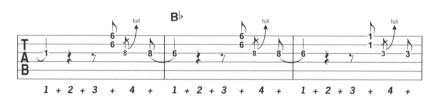

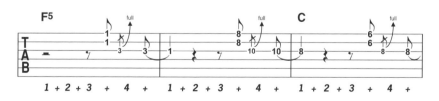

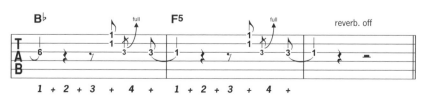

Bridge Over Troubled Water

Words & Music by Paul Simon

Capo Fret **1**

Beginner

Intermediate

Intermediate +

TAB

Intro

| D/A   A | G   A/G   G#dim7 | D/A*   B7sus4   B7 | G   Gm |

| D | G/D | D | G/D |

Verse 1

       D G/D D | G
When you're weary, feeling small,
     C G | D Dmaj7 | Em7
When tears are in your eyes
    | D   G | D G |
I will dry them all.
| D A/C# Bm | A7 A7 | D Dmaj7 |
  I'm on your side, oh when times get rough
D7 | G E | A
  And friends just can't be found,
D A | G A/G G#dim7 | D/A* B7sus4 B7 |
Like a bridge o - ver troubled water
| G A#dim7 | Bm
  I will lay me down,
 D A | G A/G G#dim7 | D/A* B7sus4 B7 |
Like a bridge o - ver troubled water
| G A#dim7 | D G/D D   G/D
  I will lay me down.

Link 1

| D | G/D | D | G/D |

Verse 2

When you're down and out,
When you're on the street,
When evening falls so hard
I will comfort you.
I'll take your part, oh when darkness comes
And pain is all around
Like a bridge over troubled water
I will lay me down,
 D A | G A/G G#dim7 | D/A* B7sus4 Bm7 |
Like a bridge o - ver troubled water
| G F# | Bm Bm(maj7) Bm7 | E
  I will lay me down.

Link 2

| D/A   A | G   Bm | G   Gm | D | G/D |

| D | G/D | D | G/D |

Beginner
Intermediate
Intermediate +
TAB

Verse 3

Sail on Silver Girl, sail on by
Your time has come to shine
All your dreams are on their way.
See how they shine, oh if you need a friend
I'm sailing right behind
Like a bridge over troubled water.
I will ease your mind,

| D   A | G   A/G G♯dim7 | D/A*   B7sus4 Bm7 |

Like a bridge o - ver   troubled water.

| G   F♯ | Bm   Bm(maj7) Bm7 | E |

    I will ease your mind.

Coda | D/A   A | G Bm | G Gm | D |

Introduction

A true evergreen hit for Simon & Garfunkel, this is a wonderful and powerful song. From the album of the same name, it was released in 1970.

Chords

This song is here because there is no guitar in it at all—that's right! But it's such a beautiful song to play that I had to include it, and part of the fun is the freedom you have to explore how to play it. I recommend starting with the most basic chord grips and very simple strumming—just simple down-strums—and work at it until you can play along with the original recording. Some of the more unusual chords are shown below to help you get going.

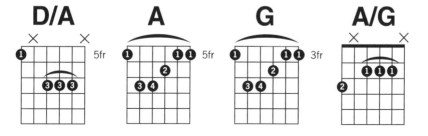

D/A   A   G   A/G

continued...

Bridge Over Troubled Water (cont.)

Beginner

Intermediate

Intermediate +

TAB

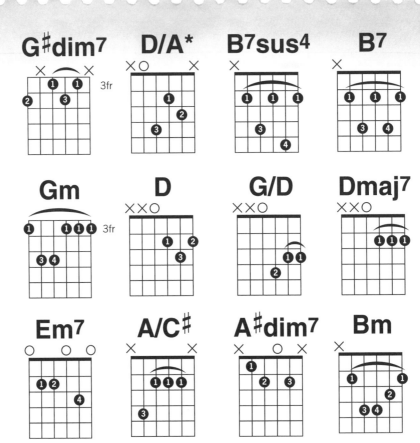

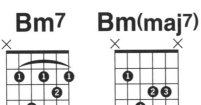 Voice Leading

Once you can strum or pick a basic version of the song, you might like to explore 'voice leading', where you think of each note in the chord as an individual voice and try to move smoothly from one chord to another without big jumps between these 'voices'. It sounds very cool and will give a piano-like flavour to your guitar playing.

108

Everybody's Talkin'
Words & Music by Fred Neil

Introduction

This is Harry Nilsson's timeless hit, recorded back in 1968, and famously featured on the *Midnight Cowboy* (1969) soundtrack. It has a very recognisable guitar part!

Fingerstyle Pattern

The fingerstyle pattern here has been the cause of great debate among guitar players since its release, but as I hear it there is more than one guitar track on the recording, which causes the confusion: there is a main guitar part and then another with a similar sound adding in single lines and notes that wouldn't be possible if there were just one guitar part.

Over the page I have tabbed out an arrangement of the main guitar part, playing the verse sequence. It is less complicated than what you hear on the record but it sounds cool for one player—of course you should feel free to experiment with it and embellish it if you like! It's a folk fingerstyle pattern (there is a whole free course on my website about this style if it interests you!) using the thumb to play alternating strings and introducing melodic elements on the thin strings. It really is a sweet sounding riff and lots of fun. Remember that once you have played this sequence, you will have played all of the chords that appear later in the song, so you can carry on playing this fingerstyle pattern throughout the song.

As usual the trick here is to start slowly—with complex fingerstyle patterns you MUST get it right at a slow speed and build up gradually. Otherwise you are likely to make a mess of it and get your fingers tied in a knot!

The chord parts are pretty simple and the fingering should be fairly obvious, although the C6 chord has a couple of fingering options. I prefer to use finger 1 on string 3 but make sure you don't hit the open string 2 if you go for this option. Alternatively you can flatten your 2nd finger to do a small two-string barre—I find this very difficult but I've seen other people do it so maybe it will work for you. Some of the changes feel a little strange but I think it sounds great all together.

Everybody's Talkin'

Words & Music by Fred Neil

Intro

| C   Cmaj7 | C   Cmaj7 | C   Cmaj7 | C   Cmaj7 |

Verse 1

| C   Cmaj7 | C   Cmaj7 |
Everybody's talkin' at me,
| C7   C6 | C7   C6
I can't hear a word they're saying,
| G7sus4/D   G7/D | Dm7   G7 | C6   C | C6   C |
Only the echoes   of my mind.
| C   Cmaj7 | C   Cmaj7 |
People stopping, staring
| C7   C6 | C7   C6 |
I can't see their faces,
| G7sus4/D   G7/D | Dm7   G7 | C6   C | C6   C |
Only the shadows of their eyes.

Chorus 1

Dm7   **G7**
I'm going where the sun keeps shining
C   **C7**
Through the pouring rain.
Dm7   **G7** | C   Cmaj7 | C7
Going where the weather suits my clothes.
Dm7   **G7**
Backing off of the North East wind,
C   **C7**
Sailing on summer breeze,
Dm7   **G7** | C   Cmaj7 | C7   C6 |
Tripping over the ocean like a stone.

Instrumental

| C   Cmaj7 | C   Cmaj7 | C7   C6 | C7   C6 |

| G7sus4/D   G7/D | Dm7   G7 | C6   C | C6   C |

Chorus 2

As Chorus 1

Verse 2

Everybody's talking at me,
I can't hear a word they're saying,
| G7sus4/D   G7/D | Dm7   G | C6   C | C6   C |
Only the echoes   of my mind.
| G7sus4/D   G7/D | Dm7   G | C6   C | C6   C |
I won't let you   leave   my love be - hind.

(Repeat ad lib. to fade)

Beginner

Intermediate

Intermediate +

TAB

Verse Sequence

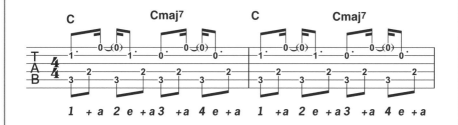

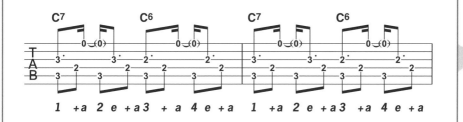

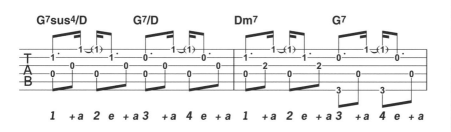

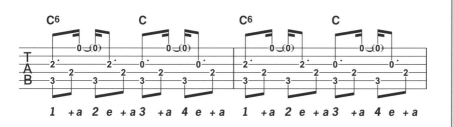

Landslide

Words & Music By Stevie Nicks

Capo
Fret
3

Intro

```
| C  G/B  | Am G/B | C  G/B  | Am G/B |
```

Verse 1

```
| C          G/B        | Am G/B
   I took my love, took it down,
| C          G/B                    | Am G/B
   I climbed a mountain, and I turned a - round,
     | C        G/B      | Am          G/B
And I saw my re - flection in the snow covered hills,
     | C        G/B      | Am     G/B |
Till the landslide brought me down.   (Oh)
```

Verse 2

Oh mirror in the sky what is love?
Can the child within my heart rise above?
Can I sail through the changing ocean tides?
Can I handle the seasons of my life?

```
| C          G/B        | Am          D7/F♯ |
   Mmmn.                    (Well I've)
```

Chorus 1

```
     | G        D7/F♯     | Em
Well I've been afraid of     changing,
       | C        G/B      | Am  D7/F♯
'Cause I've built my life around you,
     | G              D7/F♯
But time makes you bol - der,
     | Em
Even children get older,
       | C          G/B | Am G/B |
Now I'm getting older too.
```

Guitar solo

```
| C  G/B  | Am G/B | C  G/B  | Am G/B  |

| C  G/B  | Am G/B | C  G/B  | Am D7/F♯ |
```

Chorus 2

As Chorus 1

...Oh I'm getting older too.

Verse 3

Ah, take my love, take it down,
Ah, climb a mountain and turn around.
And if you see my reflection in the snow covered hills,
Will the landslide bring it down?
And if you see my reflection in the snow covered hills,
Will the landslide bring it down?
Oh, the landslide will bring it down.

Beginner

Intermediate

Intermediate +

TAB

Introduction

Landslide was a hit for Fleetwood Mac—it was written by Stevie Nicks and released in 1975 on the album *Fleetwood Mac*. The song features some lovely acoustic guitar work by Lindsey Buckingham.

Fingerstyle

To play this song confidently I would suggest you work through my online Folk Fingerstyle course (starting at FO-100) because it takes you right through the development of picking patterns like this one. The course even shows you how to improvise lines within the chords, which you should hear if you check out some of Fleetwood Mac's live recordings of the song.

The key to this style is getting the (picking hand) thumb alternating between strings and making sure it keeps a solid rhythm. The fingers are adding body to it but it's the rhythm of the thumb that will drive it along. If you are unfamiliar with the patterns used then you should start slowly and work on getting the pattern consistent, just working through simple chord changes before trying anything fancy.

There are a few guitar parts on the original recording so don't be alarmed if the part shown overleaf doesn't sound quite as complex as the original. Once you can play the main part you might like to try to add in some lines and fancy fills, but it's better to be simple and strong than to get all fancy and make mistakes!

There are a few points in the song where there are minor variations—you'll have to listen out for them as in this format I can't include every note in the song! There's nothing too tricky, just moments like the end of the verses where you'll hold the Am for an extra beat (before moving to G/B). Keep your ears open and you'll be fine.

continued...

Beginner

Intermediate

Intermediate +

TAB

Verse Pattern

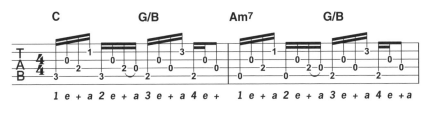

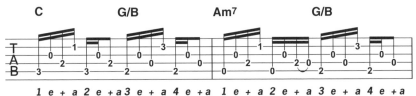

Chorus Pattern

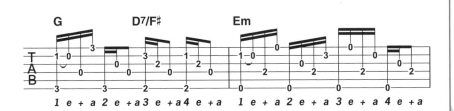

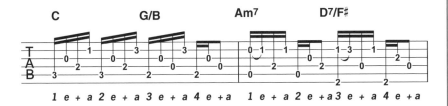

Lucy In The Sky With Diamonds

Words & Music by John Lennon & Paul McCartney

Introduction

This is the legendary Beatles song from *Sgt. Pepper's Lonely Hearts Club Band*, released in 1967, which sparked off controversy over the title's initials of L.S.D.

Intro / Verse 1

The song starts with the unique sound of a heavily effected Lowrey organ, but the part works great arranged for guitar, as shown below.

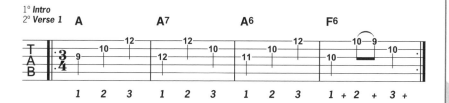

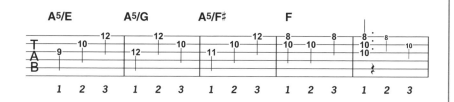

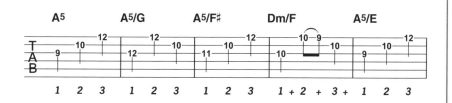

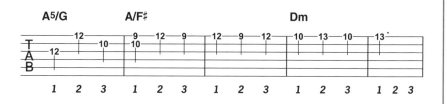

Lucy In The Sky With Diamonds

Words & Music by John Lennon & Paul McCartney

Beginner

Intermediate

Intermediate +

TAB

Intro

$\frac{3}{4}$| A | A7 | A6 | F6 |

Verse 1

```
A           A7      A6        F6
Picture yourself in a boat on a river,
      A         A7      A6          F    F
With tangerine trees and marmalade skies.
A           A7          A6          F6
Somebody calls you, you answer quite slowly,
    A         A7      A6  A6   Dm    Dm
A girl with kaleidoscope eyes.
```

Pre-chorus 1

```
Bb          Bb        C         C
Cellophane flowers of yellow and green,
F       F         Bb    Bb
Towering over your head.
C        C           G       G
Look for the girl with the sun in her eyes,
    4
    4 D
And she's gone.
```

Chorus 1

```
|G        C      |D
Lucy in the sky with diamonds,
|G        C      |D
Lucy in the sky with diamonds,
|G        C      |D
Lucy in the sky with diamonds,
D    (A)
Ah - ah.
```

Verse 2

Follow her down to a bridge by a fountain,
Where rocking horse people eat marshmallow pies.
Everyone smiles as you drift past the flowers,
That grow so incredibly high.

Pre-chorus 2

Newspaper taxis appear on the shore,
Waiting to take you away.
Climb in the back with your head in the clouds,
And you're gone.

Chorus 2

As Chorus 1

Verse 3

Picture yourself on a train in a station,
With plasticine porters with looking glass ties.
Suddenly someone is there at the turnstile,

```
    A         A7       A6   A6   4
                                 4 Dm
The girl with kaleidoscope eyes.
```

Chorus 3

As Chorus 1   *(Repeat to Fade)*

Pre-Chorus

The guitar comes in on the pre-chorus playing down-strums on all the beats, using simple barre chords. A similar vibe continues for the chorus, where the guitar plays pretty constant eighth-notes. Watch out for the little link between the pre-chorus and chorus, where the chord (D) is sustained for a bar.

If you are playing the song solo you might like to try this arrangement of the pre-chorus and chorus which is a little more interesting than just strumming.

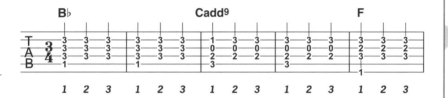

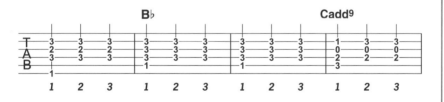

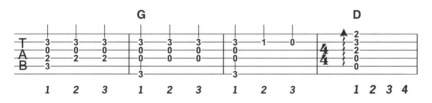

Lola

Words & Music by Ray Davies

Beginner

Intermediate

Intermediate +

TAB

Intro

| C   D | E |

Verse 1

       E
I met her in a club down in old Soho
    |A   D |E
Where you drink champagne and it tastes just like cherry-cola.
     |A   Asus⁴ A
C.O.L.A. cola.
    |E
She walked up to me and she asked me to dance,
 |A   D |E
I asked her her name and in a dark brown voice she said, 'Lola'.
     |A   D |C   D|
L.O.L.A. Lola,   la-la-la-la Lola.

Link 1

| E | E |

Verse 2

Well I'm not the world's most physical guy
But when she squeezed me tight she nearly broke my spine
Oh my Lola, la-la-la-la Lola.
Well I'm not dumb but I can't understand
Why she walked like a woman and talked like a man,
Oh my Lola, la-la-la-la Lola, la-la-la-la Lola.

Link 2

As Link 1

Bridge 1

        B
Well, we drank champagne and danced all night
F♯
Under electric candlelight.

      A
She picked me up and sat me on her knee
        Am
And said, 'Dear boy, won't you come home with me?'

Verse 3

Well, I'm not the world's most passionate guy
But when I looked in her eyes, well, I almost fell for my Lola.
La-la-la-la Lola, la-la-la-la Lola.
Lola, la-la-la-la Lola, la-la-la-la Lola.

Link 3

As Link 1

Bridge 2

|A   C♯m B |A   C♯m B
I pushed her away, I walked to the door,
|A C♯m B |E   G♯m C♯m
I fell to the floor, I got down on my knees,
     |B
Then I looked at her and she at me.

Verse 3

Well that's the way that I want it to stay
And I always want it to be that way for my Lola,
La-la-la-la Lola.
Girls will be boys and boys will be girls,
It's a mixed up muddled up shook up world except for Lola,
La-la-la-la Lola.

Bridge 3
(chords as
Bridge 1)

Well I left home just a week before
And I'd never ever kissed a woman before,
But Lola smiled and took me by the hand
And said, 'Little boy, I'm gonna make you a man.'

Verse 4

Well I'm not the world's most masculine man
But I know what I am and I'm glad I'm a man,
And so is Lola, la-la-la-la Lola, la-la-la-la Lola.

Outro

Lola, la-la-la-la Lola, la-la-la-la Lola. (Repeat to fade)

 ## Introduction

This is The Kinks' massive hit about their manager's encounter with a transvestite in a club. I must admit enjoying watching people sing along with it when they clearly don't have a clue what the song is about!

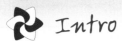 ## Intro

Even the intro to this song is distinctive—it only has only a few strummed chords but the rhythm is instantly recognisable! The last few notes are picked out but it's pretty easy overall, as long as you make sure you ace the rhythm.

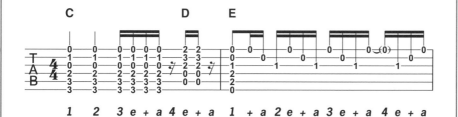

119

Verse 1

The first verse uses a mix of strumming and picking out notes one at a time—this can be a tricky technique to really nail down and there's not a lot of consistency in the patterns. So feel free to experiment a bit, using the example below as a starting point.

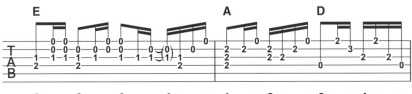

Riff

After the first verse an electric guitar comes in with another iconic lead riff which sounds awesome (and is repeated through the song), so I thought I'd get that in there too! After this the electric guitar plays chords, but more sustained than the acoustic part and with some little riffy bits thrown in for good measure.

 Bridge 2

The dynamics of the song build, and in Bridge 1 you are likely to be giving it a lot of energy and strumming quite heavily. Be aware of the energy in the song—it's a good idea to play along with the recording and follow the dynamic (volume) variations. Bridge 2 has some interesting rhythm changes going on so I thought it would be helpful to have that written out. I've just shown you the first bar, but the rest are the same—only the chords change. Remember to keep your hand moving with the sixteenth-note pattern, even though you are not playing many strums in each bar!

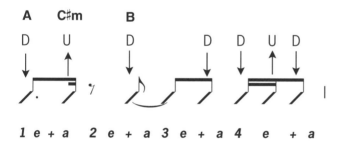

121

Oh, Pretty Woman

Words & Music by Roy Orbison & Bill Dees

Beginner

Intermediate

Intermediate +

TAB

Intro

riff 1

| Drums ‖: $\frac{4}{4}$ (E) | $\frac{2}{4}$ (E) :‖

riff 2

‖: (E) :‖ *(Play x4)*

Verse 1

      A   F♯m
Pretty woman, walking down the street,
      A   F♯m
Pretty woman, the kind I like to meet,
      D $\frac{2}{4}$ D
Pretty woman,
    $\frac{4}{4}$ E   E
I don't be - lieve you, you're not the truth,
          E   E
No-one could look as good as you.

Link 1

riff 2 (x4)
| E | E | E | E |
            Mercy!

Verse 2

Pretty woman, won't you pardon me?
Pretty woman, I couldn't help but see,
Pretty woman,
That you look lovely as can be.
Are you lonely just like me?

Link 2

riff 2 (x3)
| E | E | E | E E7 |
            Grrrowl...

Bridge

Dm   G7
   Pretty woman, stop awhile,
C   Am
   Pretty woman, talk awhile,
Dm   G7   C   C
   Pretty woman, give your smile to me.
Dm   G7
   Pretty woman, yeah yeah yeah,
C   Am
   Pretty woman, look my way,
Dm   G7   C   A
   Pretty woman, say you'll stay with me.
       F♯m   Dm   E
'Cause I   need you,   I'll treat you right.
A   F♯m   Dm   riff 2 (x4)
   Come with me baby,   be mine tonight.

Verse 3

        A   F#m
Pretty woman, don't walk on by,

        A   F#m
Pretty woman, don't make me cry,

     D $\frac{2}{4}$ D
Pretty woman,

  $\frac{4}{4}$ E   E   E
Don't walk away, hey,

     E   E   E   E   E
O - kay,   if that's the way it must be, o - kay.

          E   E
I guess I'll go on home, it's late;

         E   N.C.   **riff 1 (x2)**
There'll be tomorrow night... but wait! What do I see?

     riff 2 (x9)
Is she walking back to me?

Yeah, she's walking back to me.

        A
Oh, pretty woman.

 ## Introduction

This was a huge hit for the late great man in shades, Roy Orbison, in 1964.

 ## Intro

This song features an outstanding guitar riff which is both easy and rewarding to play, and instantly recognisable.

The intro starts with a bar of drums and then an interesting six-beat guitar figure, which outlines the first half of the main guitar riff, and is followed by two beats of solo drums. This is all played twice, before we hit the main riff in full.

Riff 1   E7

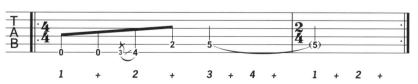

Beginner

Intermediate

Intermediate +

TAB

 Main Riff

Now we hit the big one! The riff is played four times before we get to the verse, and please be sure to take it slowly and get it right. The riff isn't hard if you approach it slowly—but if you rush through it and get your fingers in a tangle it will feel difficult, which it really isn't! You can choose to alternate-pick the riff or to use all down-strums, which from video evidence seems to be the way that Roy Orbison played it.

Riff 2

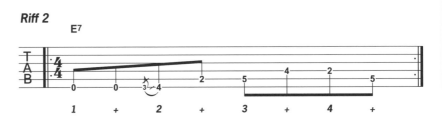

 Strumming

Once the verse kicks in we're into rhythm guitar and strumming. It sounds on the original recording like the electric is sitting out, while you can just about hear the acoustic guitar strumming away in the background. It's hard to hear exactly what pattern is being played but from watching video performances it would seem that Roy Orbison played continuous eighth-note strumming with accents on beat 2 and on the 'and' after beat 3. The 'Old Faithful' pattern will work well too, but watch out for the 2/4 bars which may throw you off balance if you are using that pattern.

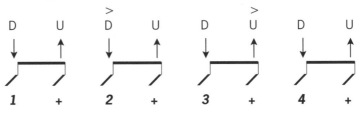

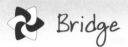 Bridge

Before the Bridge we have another verse and some more riffs and Roy's famous growl (sounds more like gurgling mouthwash to me!). In the Bridge you'll hear an acoustic guitar strumming and some spread chords (single strums at the start of each bar) on electric guitar with a gorgeous vibrato sound. The chord grips are higher up the neck than the acoustic ones and there are some tasty arpeggiated bits too!

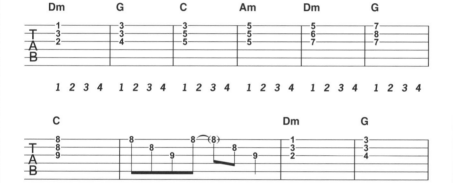

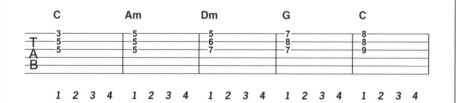

Then we've got repeats of other sections and an outro where you need to hold one chord for a bit, but it's nothing you haven't done already so get those ears out and check out the original recording!

Pinball Wizard

Words & Music by Pete Townshend

Intro

| Bm | Bmadd11 | F#7sus4 | F#7 |
| F#m7 | Em/F# | G6 | F#7 | F#7 |
‖: Bsus4 | B | Bsus4 | B :‖

Verse 1

Bsus4   Badd11
Ever since I was a young boy I've played the silver ball,
Asus2/4   Aadd9
From Soho down to Brighton I must've played them all.
G6add11   G6
But I ain't seen nothing like him in any amusement hall,
F#7sus4   N.C.
That deaf, dumb and blind kid sure plays a mean pinball.

Link

| B   A   D | E | B   A   D | E |

Verse 2

He stands like a statue, becomes part of the machine,
Feeling all the bumpers, always playing clean,
Plays by intuition, the digit counters fall,
That deaf, dumb and blind kid sure plays a mean pinball.

Link

| B   A   D | E | B   A   D | E |

Bridge 1

          | E5   F#5 B5 | E5   F#5   B5
He's a pin - ball wizard, there has to be a twist,
  | E5   F#5   B5 | G5 | D   Dsus4 | D
A pin - ball wizard's got such a supple wrist.

Middle

| D   C   G/B | D   C   G/B |
How do you think   he   does it? (*I don't   know*)
| Dsus2   Csus2 G/B | D
What makes him   so   good?

Verse 3

Ain't got no distractions, can't hear no buzzers or bells.
Don't see no lights a-flashing, plays by the sense of smell,
Always gets a 'replay', never tilts at all,
That deaf, dumb and blind kid sure plays a mean pinball.

Link

| B   A   D | E | B   A   D | E |

Bridge 2

I thought I was the bally-table king
But I just handed my pinball crown to him.

Link

‖: Dsus4 | D | Dsus4 | D :‖

Verse 4

Dsus4   D
Even at my favourite table he can beat my best,

(cont.)

          Csus⁴   **C**
His disciples lead him in, and he just does the rest,
        B♭sus⁴   **B♭**
He's got crazy flipper fingers, never see him fall,
        Asus⁴   **N.C.**
That deaf, dumb and blind kid sure plays a mean pinball.

Coda | D   C F ‖: B♭7 | B♭7 :‖   *Repeat to fade*

 ## Introduction

This is the most famous song from the Who's rock opera and album *Tommy* (1969). It has loads of awesome guitar parts to get your teeth into.

 ### Intro

The first section of the intro consists of an F♯ pedal note with chords ringing out on top. There are a couple of layers of guitar here but I'm just showing you the main part (which is panned to the right speaker). I can't say for sure, but the delayed part in the left speaker sounds like it's just an effected version of the main guitar part.

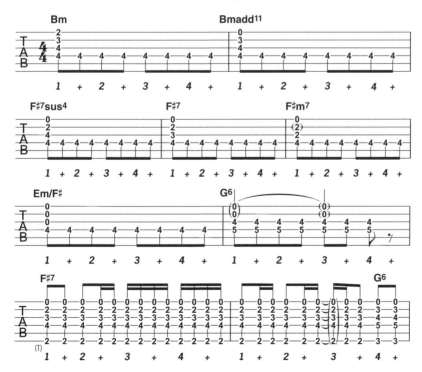

127

Beginner

Intermediate

Intermediate +

TAB

♫ Intro (cont.)

The acoustic guitar then kicks off with a very specific strumming pattern which is used through the verses too. I'd recommend spending a bit of time on this next bit and really nailing the rhythm before starting work on the verse—it'll be a lot easier if you practise it this way! Follow the rhythm pattern shown in the TAB below carefully and remember to keep your hand moving consistently all the way through; that really is the key to getting this part sounding ace. The electric guitar just plays a single note riff—it's simple enough that I'm going to leave it for you to figure out!

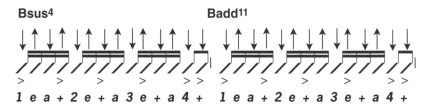

Now that you have the rhythm sorted you can apply that same groove to the verses, where the chords start changing more regularly. You'll hear the electric guitar in the left speaker hitting some power chords too.

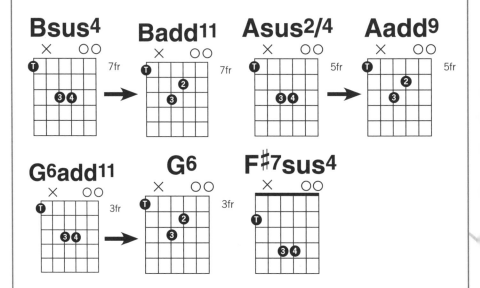

Beginner

Intermediate

Intermediate +

TAB

Link / Verse 4 Chords

Dsus4 → **D**
10fr

Csus4 → **C**
8fr

B♭sus4 → **B♭**
6fr

Asus4
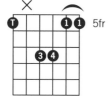
5fr

Beginner

Intermediate

Intermediate +

TAB

Riff

At the end of the verse we have the song's famous riff. The electric and acoustic guitars are playing very similar things and the big deal here is to really nail the rhythm and get it tight. The acoustic guitar part is shown below although the electric guitar part is more or less the same, just slightly less busy. I'm sure you'll be able to hear it on the original recording.

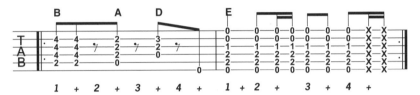

Chorus

We then have another verse and a repeat of the famous riff before we hit the chorus. The chorus has more complex rhythms which you'll have to get to grips with. As usual the best strategy is to play it slowly and carefully and only start speeding it up when you are confident that you have it right. Counting along with the rhythm and also listening repeatedly to the original recording are the best ways to learn more complex passages like this one!

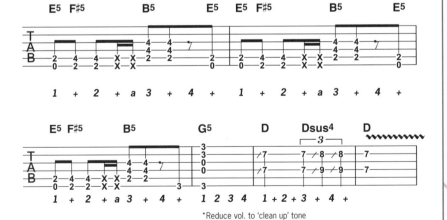

*Reduce vol. to 'clean up' tone

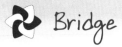 Bridge

Following the chorus comes a short Bridge section, which mainly involves picked strumming on the acoustic guitar.

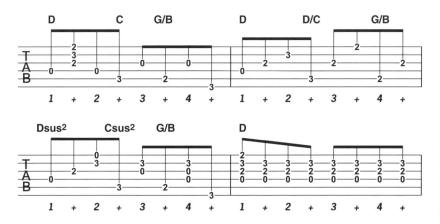

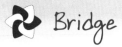 Outro

The following verse has the same acoustic part but an interesting muted part comes in on the electric guitar, all on one note (a B)! After some repetitions of sections we've already discussed, there is a repeat of the main riff, now transposed to D, and slightly altered. Then there is a short and slightly trippy outro which I'm writing out here because it's so cool. Pete Townsend is really an outstanding guitar player!

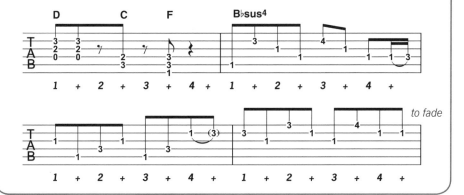

131

Carol

Words & Music by Chuck Berry

Beginner

Intermediate

Intermediate +

TAB

Intro

| B♭ | E♭7 | B♭ | B♭ N.C. |

Oh...

Chorus 1

E♭   E♭   B♭   B♭
Carol, don't let him steal your heart a - way,

      F   E♭   B♭   B♭
I'm gonna learn to dance if it takes me all night and day.

Verse 1

        B♭   B♭   B♭   B♭
Climb into my machine so we can groove on out,

        B♭   B♭   B♭   B♭
I knows a swingin' little joint where we can jump and shout.

        E♭   E♭   E♭   E♭
It's not too far back off the highway, not so long a ride,

        B♭   B♭   B♭   B♭
You park your car out in the open, you can walk inside.

      F   F   F   F
A little cutie takes your hat and you can thank her, ma'am,

      B♭   B♭   B♭   B♭
Every time you make the scene you find the joint is jammed.

Link 1

As Intro

Chorus 2

As Chorus 1

Link 2

As Intro

Chorus 3
(instrumental)

| E♭ | E♭ | B♭ | B♭ | |

| F | E♭ | B♭ | B♭ F7 |

Verse 2

Now if you wanna hear some music like the boys are playin',
Hold tight, pat your foot, don't let it carry you away.
Don't let the heat overcome you when they play so loud,
Why, don't the music intrigue you when they get a crowd.
You can't dance, I know you would you could,
I got my eyes on you baby, 'cause you dance so good.

Link 3

As Intro

Chorus 4

E♭   E♭   B♭   B♭
Carol, don't let him steal your heart a - way,

      F   E♭   B♭   F
I'm gonna learn to dance if it takes me all night and day.

Link 4

As Intro

Chorus 5	As Chorus 1

	B♭ B♭
Outro	Oh, girl! *(Repeat to fade)*

 Introduction

Here we're looking at the Rolling Stones cover of Chuck Berry's 'Carol', released by the Stones on their eponymous debut album in 1964.

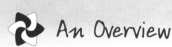 An Overview

Before evolving into a stadium rock band, the Rolling Stones were at the heart of the London R&B scene, and this recording really shows how dedicated The Stones were to imitating the blues masters. This song is a lesson on how to play in the Chuck Berry-style, and is played with authenticity and great energy. Of course Keith Richards adds his own unique style to the mix as well.

Songs like this rarely come off the page well and are best learned by listening to the record while following the tab so you can get a feel for how the two relate to each other. Often you'll find that the notes don't look right at first, but they are, you just have to play them with the right feel, which is one of the things you'll only really pick up by listening to the recording.

The rhythm part is played using a barre chord 12-bar blues shuffle pattern (taught in my free Blues Rhythm Guitar course on the website!) but it's worth noting that bands of this era often kept the root note on the 6th string and shifted the chord right up the dusty end of the neck rather than moving over a string. It makes it easier in some ways and more difficult in others, but what it does—and which can't be replicated any other way—is sound right!

Over the page I've transcribed the first 50 seconds (up to Chorus 2) of the lead guitar part so you can learn the intro and many of the classic licks that Keith Richards uses between the vocal lines. Note that there are some licks behind the vocals that are very quiet on the recording (barely audible!), which I have included (as best I could) in the transcription. I remember learning lots of licks from this track in my early teens and if you are familiar with basic blues licks and have done a little transcribing before then this is a great song to get stuck into. It's not super easy, but you will learn a lot in the process.

continued...

Carol (cont.)

Words & Music by Chuck Berry

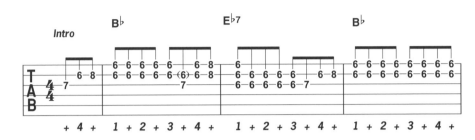

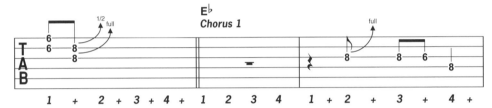

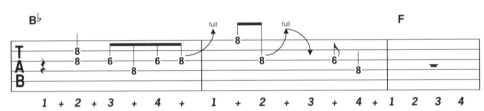

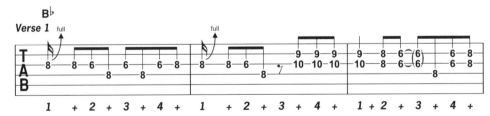

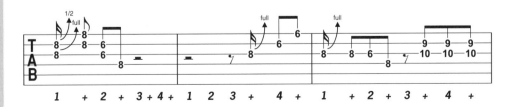

134

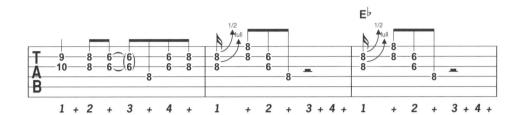

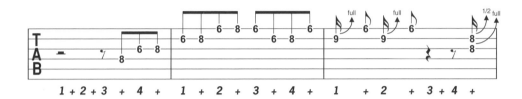

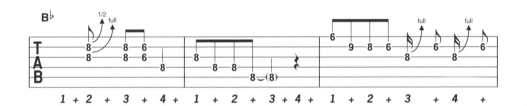

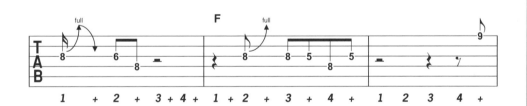

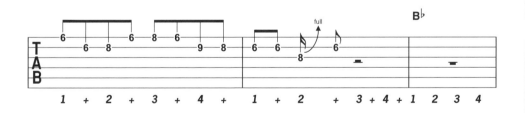

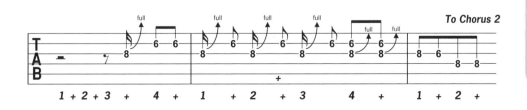

These Days
Words & Music by Jackson Browne

Capo Fret
5

Beginner

Intermediate

Intermediate +

TAB

Intro

‖: C C(add9)/B Am7 C/G | Fmaj7 :‖

Verse 1

(Fmaj7) | C   C(add9)/B Am7   C/G | Fmaj7
Well,   I've been out   walk - ing,
    | C C(add9)/B Am7 C/G | Fmaj7
I don't do that much talk - ing   these days,
    C   G
These days.
    Fmaj7
These days I seem to think a lot
    Fmaj7   C |G   E7
A - bout the things that I forgot to do for you.
   | Am7 G | Fmaj7
And all   the times I had the chance to.

Link

| C C(add9)/B | Am7 C/G | Fmaj7 | Fmaj7 |

Verse 2

(Fmaj7) | C C(add9)/B Am7 C/G | Fmaj7
And   I had a   lover,
    | C   C(add9)/B Am7 C/G | Fmaj7
But it's so hard to risk   an - other   these days,
    C   G
These days.
    Fmaj7
Now if I seem to be afraid
    Fmaj7   C |G E7
To live the life that I have made in song,
    | Am7 G | Fmaj7
Well, it's just that I've been los - ing
    | C C(add9)/B Am7   C/G | Fmaj7
For so_____ long.

Instr.

C C(add9)/B Am7 C/G	Fmaj7
C	G
Fmaj7	Fmaj7
C	G E7
Am7 Em7	Fmaj7

Verse 3

Well, I'll keep on moving, moving on,
Things are bound to be improving these days,
One of these days.

(cont.)	These days I'll sit on corner stones And count the time in quarter tones to ten, my friend. Don't confront me with my failures, I had not forgotten them.

Outro   ‖: C C(add9)/B │ Am7 C/G │ Fmaj7 │ Fmaj7 :‖ (Play x12)
│ C   │

Introduction

This is one of Jackson Browne's most popular songs, written when he was sixteen years old. Although there's a famous recording of the song by Nico, we're looking at Browne's own version from 1973, which is much more guitar-centred.

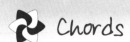

Chords

This lovely song has an unusual quirk, which you'll need to keep an eye out for when performing it! The first important thing to check out is the series of chords used in the intro, which are repeated at various points in the song. The chords are linked by a descending bass line, so make sure you are aware of that.

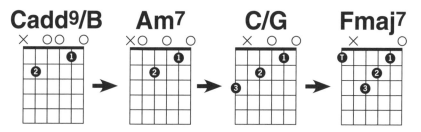

The key to getting the changes smooth is keeping your first finger down all the way—this should help you guide the rest of your fingers. From the C you'll just need to move your 2nd finger up a string (to the fifth string) and remove your 3rd finger for the Cadd9/B (complex name, easy chord). For the Am7, just move your 2nd finger back where it was and leave the fifth string open. To get to the C/G just add your 3rd finger down on the 3rd fret of the thickest string. Lastly you'll need your 'thumb over' F. I suspect that this F chord will be tricky for many of you—the 'secret' to being able to play 'thumb over' chords is perseverance. Everybody seems to grab it a slightly different way, depending on their hand and finger shapes, but stick with it if you really want to crack it. You can play an easier Fmaj7 by simply leaving out the bass note.

137

 Rhythm

The strumming on this song is delicate, and varied – it's so sensitively played that to force a certain pattern on it seems vulgar, but I'll give you a starting point. Remember that to really get these tunes sounding and feeling great you need to put some of yourself into the song too—try to 'feel' the vibe of the song and let that out as you play. Start off with the pattern shown below, which is pretty much what is played in the intro. Then start playing it softly and gently and you'll probably notice some of the notes drop out, which is absolutely fine! You'll keep this as a general pattern through the song, but obviously you should build it up during the 'bigger' sections of the song, such as the instrumental.

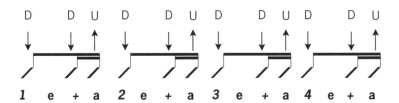

 Quirk Alert

Now the BIG QUIRK happens in the verses: the first time is in Verse 1, in the bar with the words 'all the times I had the chance'. The strange thing that happens is that the chord changes from the Am to the G on **BEAT 2**. This is very unusual because it feels like the chord will change on beat 3 like it did in the last bar, but it doesn't. You should start by getting really familiar with the song—if you can't hear it in your head, you'll just be guessing what it sounds like! Then count the beats along a few times with the song, and check out how the change sounds on beat 2—the rhythm becomes sparse there too, which adds to the instability. It's not hard, it's just unusual and is likely to take you a few goes to get it sorted!

Wouldn't It Be Nice

Words & Music by Brian Wilson, Tony Asher & Mike Love

Introduction

This is the opening track from the legendary *Pet Sounds* album by The Beach Boys, recorded back in 1966.

Arranging For Guitar

The original recording doesn't obviously feature any guitar, but it's a lot of fun to play, and full of enough interesting chords to give you a proper workout! There are also some tempo changes, which will keep you on your toes. The intro is on a string instrument—possibly a harp, possibly a 12-string guitar, although it's so heavily effected that it's hard to tell.

I would recommend starting by playing through the chords and getting to grips (literally) with any that you don't know. Then have a try at playing along with the original recording and getting a feel for its structure and where you might play what.

There is a lot of complex harmony flying around in the vocal arrangements and in the instrumentation. However, I suspect that you'll just want play the song and sing along—even if you wish to take it further you should start by keeping things simple.

The intro 'harp' section appears twice in the track but you're more likely to learn it as 'an intro' I think, so here is a guitar arrangement of it for you to learn.

Intro

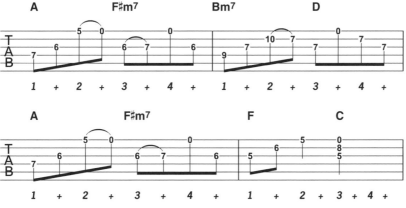

Wouldn't It Be Nice
Words & Music by Brian Wilson, Tony Asher & Mike Love

Intro

| A F#m7 | Bm7 D | A F#m7 | F (C) | |

Verse 1

```
(C)                F                 F
Wouldn't it be nice if we were older,
                 Bb              |Gm
Then we wouldn't have to wait so long,
        C           |F            F
And wouldn't it be nice to live to - gether,
              Bb              |Gm      C |
In the kind of world where we be - long.
Dm/A                          Eb/F
   You know it's gonna make it that much better,
Dm/A                          Am     Gm     C
   When we can say good night and stay to - gether.
```

Verse 2

```
Wouldn't it be nice if we could wake up,
In the morning when the day is new,
And after having spent the day together,
Hold each other close the whole night through.
Happy times together we'd be spending,
I wish that every kiss was never-ending.
              F          F
Wouldn't it be nice?
```

Bridge

```
Dmaj7          Gmaj7
   Maybe if we think and wish and hope and pray,
 F#m7              Bm7
It might come true.
Dmaj7          Gmaj7                      F#m7        Bm7
   Maybe then there wouldn't be a single thing we couldn't do.
         F#m7/C#          Bm7
We could be married, (we could be married)
             F#m7/C#                  C
And then we'd be happy, (and then we'd be happy)
             F        F      F    F
Ah, wouldn't it be nice.
```

Link
(slower tempo)

| F | F | |

Verse 3

```
Dm/A                          Eb/F
   You know it seems the more we talk about it,
Dm/A                    Am       Gm
   It only makes it worse to live with  - out it,
        Am    Gm     C
But let's talk a - bout it,
```

(a tempo)

            F   **F** **F** **F**
Wouldn't it be nice.

Outro

$\lVert$: **F**   **F**   **F**   **F**
    Good night, baby,   sleep tight, baby. :$\rVert$ *Repeat to fade*

Chords

The verses feature a couple of new chords, while the Bridge is full of more complex jazz chords which I've written for you below so you can have a play with them.

Dm/A   E♭/F

Dmaj⁷   Gmaj⁷   F♯m⁷

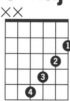

Bm⁷   F♯m⁷/C♯

141

Waterloo Sunset
Words & Music by Ray Davies

Beginner

Intermediate

Intermediate +

TAB

Intro

| B7 | B7 | B7 | B7 |

| E | B7 | A | A |

Verse 1

(A)   E   B7
    Dirty old river, must you keep rolling
          A   A
Flowing into the night?
           E   B7
People so busy, make me feel dizzy,
          A   A
Taxi light shines so bright.

Chorus 1

         F#m   F#m/F   F#m/E   B7
But I don't   need no friends
              E   B7
As long as I gaze on Waterloo sunset
        A |A
I am in paradise.

Bridge 1

(A)   A/G#   F# | F#   F#   B7 |E
(Sha- la- la)   Every day I look at the world from my window.
  A   A/G#   F# | F#   F#
(Sha- la- la)   But chilly, chilly is the evening time,
  B7   B7   B7   B7
Waterloo sunset's fine, (Waterloo sunset's fine.)

Verse 2

Terry meets Julie, Waterloo Station,
Every Friday night.
But I am so lazy, don't want to wander,
I stay at home at night.

Chorus 2

But I don't feel afraid
As long as I gaze on Waterloo sunset
I am in paradise.

Bridge 2

As Bridge 1

Verse 3

Millions of people swarming like flies 'round
Waterloo Underground,
But Terry and Julie cross over the river
Where they feel safe and sound.

Chorus 3

And they don't need no friends
As long as they gaze on Waterloo sunset
They are in paradise.

Link	E	B7	A	

Outro B7   B7

Waterloo sunset's fine.   *(Repeat to fade)*

 Introduction

This song was a massive hit for The Kinks in 1967. I was on Waterloo bridge watching a sunset recently and it really is special—I highly recommend it if you visit London in the autumn!

 Intro

The intro is an interesting mix of a guitar staying on one note while a bass descends beneath it, which then moves into the guitar playing the main melody line while the acoustic guitar plays beneath it. It's a device also used in the Bridge. I've written out a guitar arrangement of the intro that encompasses both parts in case you are playing solo.

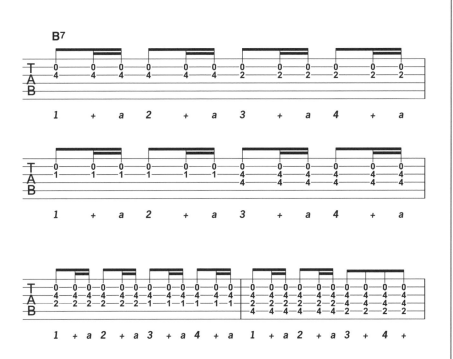

143

The Riff

I couldn't include this tune without featuring the song's famous riff:

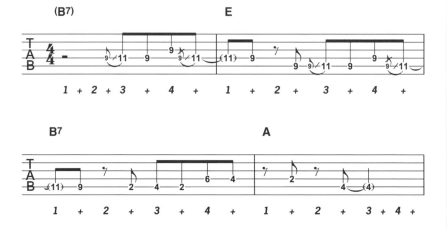

Strumming

Once the verse kicks in the acoustic guitar settles on the following strumming pattern, with some small variations. However, for the most part, this is the strumming pattern:

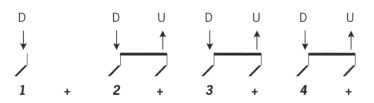

Beginner

Intermediate

Intermediate +

TAB

Chords

You will encounter a few interesting chords too—here are some chord boxes to help you out with the tricky ones. Note that this chord sequence is really F♯m, F♯m(maj7)/F, F♯m7/E. You can probably tell why we've simplified the chord names!

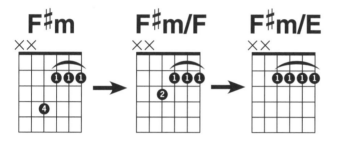

Bridge

There are also a few tricky rhythms to work on—make sure you listen to the original recording and count out any difficult sections because that will make them a lot easier. The chord stabs that lead into the Bridge start on the 3rd beat, and are mainly off the beat. If you try counting along you will find it makes more sense and will enable you to learn more complex rhythmic passages faster and play them better!

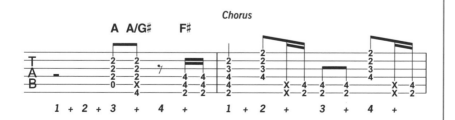

145

Wipe Out

Music by Ron Wilson, James Fuller, Bob Berryhill & Pat Connolly

Beginner

Intermediate

Intermediate

Intermediate +

TAB

Intro

Spoken: *He He He He, Wipeout!*

Drums	Bass
4	2
|—————	|—————	

Verse 1
(Riff)

| C | C | C | C |

| F | F | C | C |

| G | F | C | G |

Chorus 1
(Stops)

| C | C | C | C |

| F | F | C | C |

| G | F | C | N.C. |

Verse 2   As Verse 1

Chorus 2   As Chorus 1

Verse 3   Chords as Verse 1

Chorus 3   As Chorus 1

Verse 4   As Verse 1 *(Fade Out)*

Introduction

This track is a surf classic from The Surfaris, released in 1963. The riff is awesome fun to play on the guitar and if you play in a band, your drummer will love you for learning it as the drum part is one of the most famous ever! It's possible that the original recording was played in B and then sped up, altering the pitch, or that the guitars were tuned up a semitone. We'll be keeping the song in C, as that's the key that it's most often played in.

 Riff

The main riff is a great little line that uses a mixture of blues and chromatic notes and which falls easily under the fingers. For most people the hardest bit to sort out is the picking. You should pick the notes that fall on the beat with a down-pick and the rest (off-beats) with an up-pick. This means that the main riff will start with an up-pick. Watch out for the bar of G, where there is a stop on beat 4 (you'll end up playing two down-picks in a row, on beats 4 and 1). However, all the rest of it uses alternate-picking.

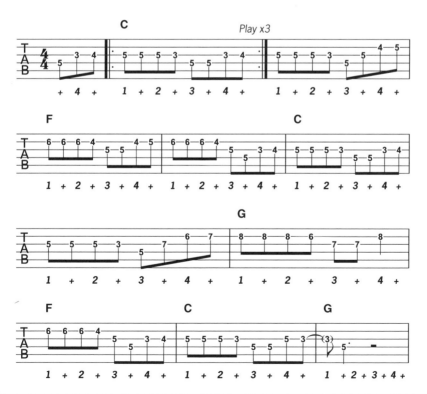

Beginner

Intermediate

Intermediate +

TAB

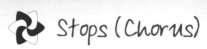

Stops (Chorus)

The other section for the rhythm guitar is the stops, which appear in the chorus, and for which you should keep the chords short and tight so they don't ring out for long at all.

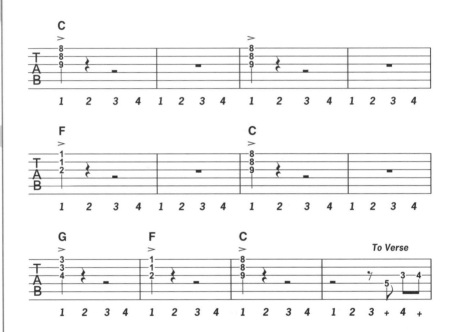

Solo

There is a cool solo to look at too—it's based primarily on the
Pentatonic scale and requires a lot of double stopping.

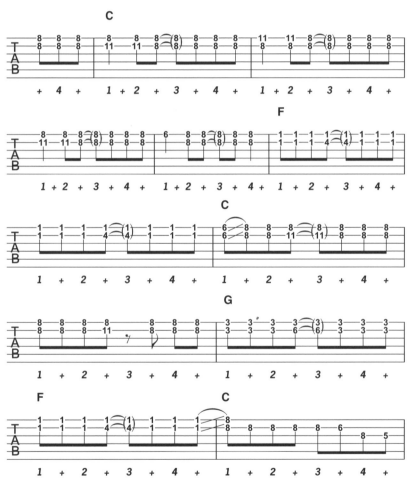

After the solo the track rips into the main drum riff again before bringing
back the riff. The guitar entry on the original recording is a little sloppy
(so maybe don't copy that bit!) but the vibe is great and that's what's
awesome about the golden days of music, when the vibe was king, not
playing absolutely flawlessly!

Beginner

Intermediate

Intermediate +

TAB

You've Got A Friend

Words & Music by Carole King

Capo Fret
2

Beginner

Intermediate

Intermediate +

TAB

Intro

| G | C C/D | Gsus⁴ G | F♯m B⁷sus⁴ B⁷ |

Verse 1

(B⁷sus⁴) (B⁷)   Em   B⁷ |Em   B⁷ |Em⁷
When   you're down and troubled and you need a helping hand,

      Am⁷   D⁷sus⁴ |G   Gsus⁴ |G
And nothing, whoa, nothing is going right.

F♯m⁷ |B⁷   B⁷sus⁴ | Em   B⁷ |Em⁷
Close your eyes and think of me   and soon I will be there

      Am⁷   Bm⁷   D⁷sus⁴   D⁷
To brighten up even your darkest nights.

Chorus 1

(D⁷)   G   Gmaj⁷   C |Am⁷
You just call out my name   and you know wherever I am,

D⁷sus⁴ |G⁶   Gmaj⁷   D⁷sus⁴ D⁷sus⁴
I'll come running, oh yeah baby, to see you again.

G   Gmaj⁷ C   Em
Winter, spring, summer or fall,   all you got to do is call

      |C   G/B |C/D D⁷sus⁴   (G)
And I'll be there,   yeah, yeah, yeah,   you've got a friend.

Link

| G | C | Gsus⁴ G | F♯m B⁷sus⁴ B⁷ |

Verse 2

If the sky above you should turn dark and full of clouds
And that old north wind should begin to blow,
Keep your head together and call my name out loud.
Soon I will be knocking upon your door.

Chorus 2

You just call out my name and you know where ever I am,
I'll come running, oh yes I will, to see you again.
Winter, spring, summer or fall, all you have to do is call
And I'll be there, yeah, yeah, yeah.

Bridge

            F   C
Hey, ain't it good to know that you've got a friend

      |G   Gsus⁴ |Gmaj⁷
When people can be so   cold?

            C   Fmaj⁷
They'll hurt you and de - sert you.

         Em⁷ |A⁷   A⁷sus² |
Well, they'll take your soul if you let them,

            D⁷sus⁴   D⁷
Oh yeah, but don't you let them.

Chorus 3

As Chorus 1

Outro

```
              G          C
(You've got a friend.)
              G              C
You've got a friend, yeah.
                              G
Ain't it good to know you've got a friend.
     C                        G
Ain't it good to know you've got a friend.
     C                     | Gsus⁴  G |
Oh, yeah, yeah, you've got a friend.
```

 # Introduction

James Taylor's beautiful cover of this Carole King song was a huge hit in 1971, winning Grammy Awards for both of them, and remains a very popular song with acoustic guitar players.

Intro / Link

James Taylor is one of the finest acoustic guitar players to have graced this planet and you can really hear it on this recording. He uses quite unconventional fingerings for the chords but you'll often find that you can substitute these with standard chord grips.

The intro is an all-time classic and instantly recognisable. The trick is to learn it slowly and carefully and make sure you have both the notes, fingering for both hands and the rhythms correct before you speed it up.

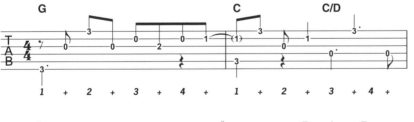

Verse 1

Chorus 1

🎋 Verse / Chorus

The guitar parts in the verse and chorus are quite a complex affair, especially if you want to get them just like the recording. There are many intricate guitar lines beneath the vocal, alongside quite complex fingerpicking and interesting chords, but you can simplify it to strumming too; just using 'Old Faithful' will work perfectly well, especially if you want to sing. Singing and playing complex fingerstyle parts will take a lot of practice as the guitar part must be practised until you can play it without thinking about it at all! I have written out a verse and a chorus for you to study and get some ideas from James Taylor's wonderful playing—you may want to steal the ideas and even the exact phrases so you can use them in other songs too!

Your Song

Words & Music by Elton John & Bernie Taupin

Capo Fret **1**

Beginner

Intermediate

Intermediate +

TAB

Intro

| D   G/D | A/D   G/D |

Verse 1

| D   Gmaj7 | A/C♯   F♯m |
It's a little bit funny,   this feeling in - side,
| Bm   Bm/A | G♯m7♭5   G6 |
I'm not one of those who can   easily hide.
| D/A   A | F♯/A♯   Bm |
I don't have much money, but   boy if I did,
| D   Em $\frac{2}{4}$| G $\frac{4}{4}$| A   Asus4   A |
I'd buy a big house where   we both could live.

Verse 2

| D   Gmaj7 | A/C♯   F♯m |
If I was a sculptor,   but then again, no,
  | Bm   Bm/A | G♯m7♭5   G6 |
Or a man who makes potions in a   travelling show.
| D/A   A | F♯/A♯   Bm |
I know it's not much, but it's the best I can do,
| D   Em $\frac{2}{4}$| G $\frac{4}{4}$| D   Dsus4   D |
My gift is my song and   this one's for you.

Chorus 1

| A/C♯   Bm | Em   G |
And you can tell everybody   this is your song.
| A/C♯   Bm | Em   G |
It may be quite simple but   now that it's done,
| Bm   Bm/A |
I hope you don't mind,   I hope you don't mind
| G♯m7♭5   G6 $\frac{2}{4}$| G6 |
That I put down in words
  $\frac{4}{4}$| D/F♯   G $\frac{2}{4}$| G $\frac{4}{4}$| A   Asus4   A |
How wonderful life is while you're in the world.

Link

| D   G/D | A/D   G/D |

Verse 3

I sat on the roof and kicked off the moss,
Well a few of the verses, well they've got me quite cross.
But the sun's been quite kind while I wrote this song,
It's for people like you that keep it turned on.

Verse 4

So excuse me forgetting, but these things I do,
You see I've forgotten if they're green or they're blue.
Anyway the thing is, what I really mean,
Yours are the sweetest eyes I've ever seen.

Chorus 2

As Chorus 1

Chorus 3	I hope you don't mind, I hope you don't mind that I put down in words |**D/F♯** **G** **²/₄**|**G** **⁴/₄**|**(D)** How wonderful life is while you're in the world.
Outro	| **D** **G/D** | **A/D** **G/D** | **D** |

 ## Introduction

Elton John and Bernie Taupin sure know how to write a hit song, and this tune seems to be just as popular now as when it was released in 1970.

Chords

Though there are some layers of guitar in this song, it's essentially a piano ballad and one that works beautifully on guitar. There are some fairly complex chord grips that you'll learn in the process, and which I'm sure you'll come across in other songs too. Step one is to play through the chords of the song and learn any that you don't know.

Make sure you memorise these chord grips as it's very important that they are in your head and not just on the page. Learn them in the order that you need them to play the song and try to put them together, using very basic strumming. If you find any particular changes very difficult then spend some time changing between the two chords for a minute (some of you will know this as 'One Minute Changes' from my Beginner's Course).

G/D
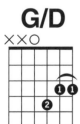

A/D

Gmaj7
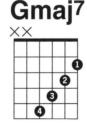

A/C♯
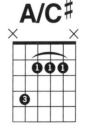

continued...

Beginner

Intermediate

Intermediate +

TAB

Beginner

Intermediate

Intermediate +

TAB

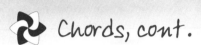

Chords, cont.

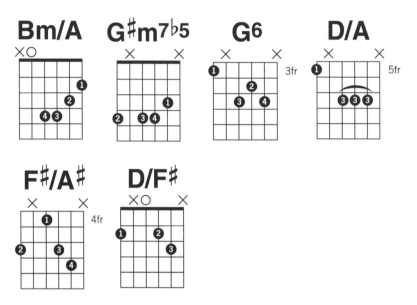

Fingerstyle

Once you have the chords and can play through them simply, I'd recommend you try applying a fingerstyle pattern to them. As long as you are playing the bass note with your thumb on beat 1 (or each new chord change) you are pretty free to pick out other chord tones as you like in between, though you'll probably find it easier to have some kind of pattern to start off. Doing T 1 2 3 / T 1 2 3 with your thumb on the bass string and the other fingers on any other fretted notes would be a good start and you can start to explore it more as you get better at it. It will make the guitar sound a little closer to a piano too.

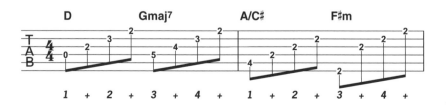

Beginner

Intermediate

Intermediate +

TAB

 ## Introduction

In the last section of this book we have a full TAB section. Here I've picked one great song and four awesome instrumentals for you to work on in much more detail.

With all these songs you should practise them slowly and carefully, making sure you are playing correctly before speeding them up. Practising slowly is the key to playing quickly!

I hope you enjoy these classics as much as I do.

TAB Guide

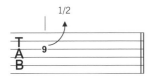

SEMI-TONE BEND: Strike the note and bend up a semi-tone (½ step).

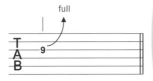

WHOLE-TONE BEND: Strike the note and bend up a whole-tone (full step).

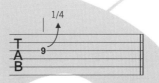

QUARTER-TONE BEND: Strike the note and bend up a ¼ step

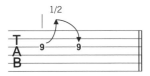

BEND & RELEASE: Strike the note and bend up as indicated, then release back to the original note.

MUFFLED STRINGS: A percussive sound is produced by laying the first hand across the string(s) without depressing, and striking them with the pick hand.

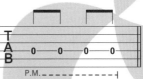

PALM MUTING: The note is partially muted by the pick hand lightly touching the string(s) just before the bridge.

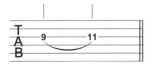

HAMMER-ON: Strike the first note with one finger, then sound the second note (on the same string) with another finger by fretting it without picking.

FLICK-OFF: Place both fingers on the note to be sounded, strike the first note and without picking, flick the finger off to sound the second note.

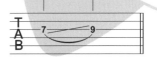

LEGATO SLIDE (GLISS): Strike the first note and then slide the same fret-hand finger up or down to the second note. The second note is not struck.

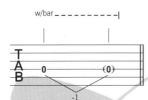

VIBRATO DIVE BAR AND RETURN: The pitch of the note or chord is dropped a specific number of steps (in rhythm) then returned to the original pitch.

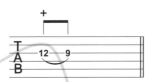

TAPPING: Hammer ('tap') the fret indicated with the pick-hand index or middle finger and flick-off to the note fretted by the fret hand.

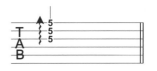

ARPEGGIATE: Play the notes of the chord indicated by quickly rolling them from bottom to top.

RAKE: Drag the pick across the strings with a single motion.

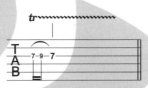

TRILL: Very rapidly alternate between the notes indicated by continuously hammering-on and flicking-off.

PINCH HARMONIC: The note is fretted normally and a harmonic is produced by adding the edge of the thumb or the tip of the index finger of the pick hand to the normal pick attack.

Apache

Music by Jerry Lordan

Introduction

Was there anybody out there who didn't want a red Stratocaster after Hank Marvin and The Shadows hit the top of the charts with this tune in 1960? Surely not.

Intro (A)

This song is a lot of fun to learn—the parts are not very complicated, and the tone is quite achievable. As usual the best way to start learning a song like this is by repeated listening, to really get the rhythm feel and style in your mind.

It's interesting to note that the rhythm guitar is panned hard right, so listening to just the left speaker will get rid of the rhythm guitar completely and allow you to hear the lead part clearly (with the bass and drums). The other speaker keeps the lead guitar but removes the drums and bass so you can get a good listen to the rhythm part when it's time to check that out!

Main Melody (B)

The main 16-bar melody is not at all complicated, sounds great and is very memorable. You will probably want to use all down-picks and remember to let the melody 'breathe'—mute the strings when there is a rest shown.

Gallop (C)

Next up we have the famous Shadows gallop! The trick with this bit is making sure the picking is Down, Down, Up—you can see the rhythm written onto the tab is groups of 3 notes. You must ensure that you follow the pattern or it will all go horribly wrong! You will also need to use a light palm mute near the bridge to deaden the string a little.

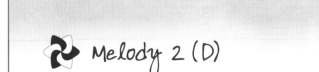

Melody 2 (D)

The next melody features some awesome whammy bar work, and as a result, the main feature—the lick in bars 7 and 8—can be very tricky to get sounding just like the record. The sound is created through a mixture of whammy bar and a vintage tape delay effect, and without that effect it never sounds quite right. Some people find the rhythm of this part a little tricky so pay special attention to that too.

The Tone

To get the tone right for this song you will need to start with a Fender Stratocaster: anything else just won't do I'm afraid! For your amp, you just need to have a good clean sound. I believe that Hank Marvin used a Vox AC15 but I've got a close sound using a clean Fender amp. The most important ingredients you'll need are delay and reverb, the delay being a tape delay or an emulation thereof. Seeing as most of you are unlikely to have a Meazzi tape echo machine (a rare Italian brand of valve tape echo machines that Hank used!) I'll assume many of you will be using a digital or analogue delay. Because of the huge differences between units I can only suggest that you find the 'tape' mode if your delay unit has one, set the time somewhere between long and medium and see what happens! I'll add some more setting advice on my site when I do the video lesson for this song.

You will also need to pick nearer the bridge than usual to get the tone right, but you will need to experiment with your picking position as it seems that different guitars react differently.

Apache
Music by Jerry Lordan

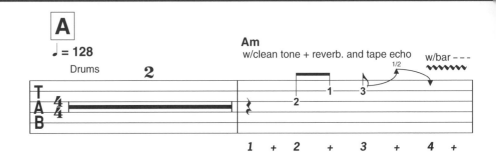

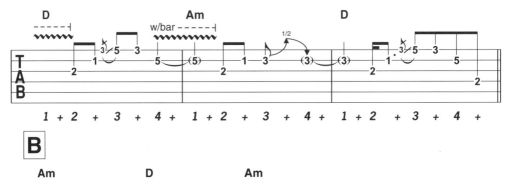

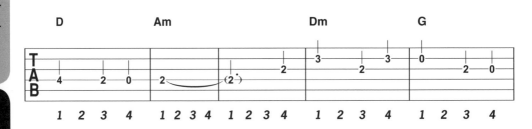

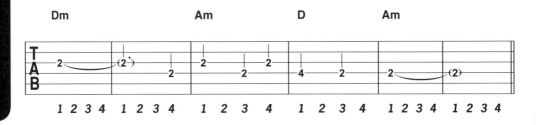

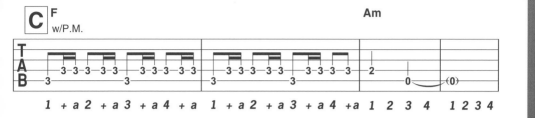

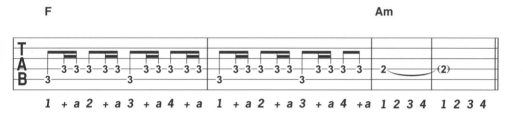

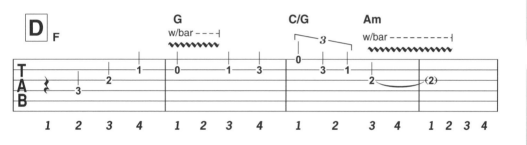

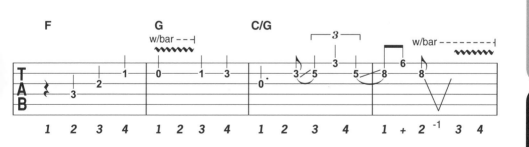

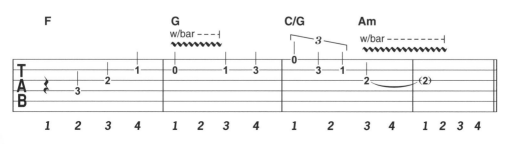

Apache (cont.)

Beginner

Intermediate

Intermediate +

TAB

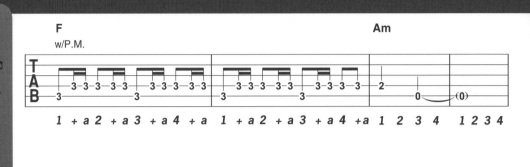

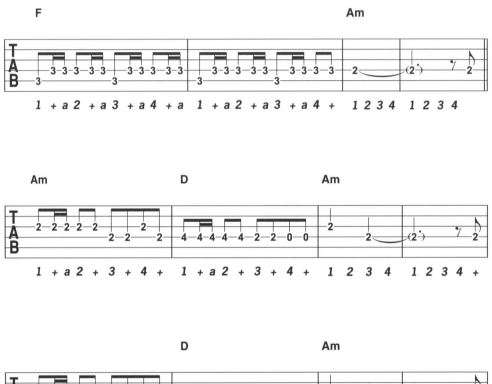

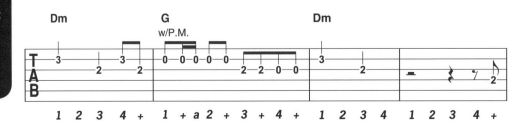

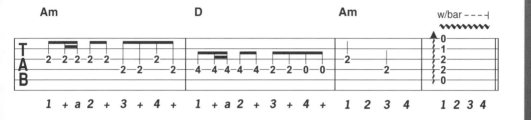

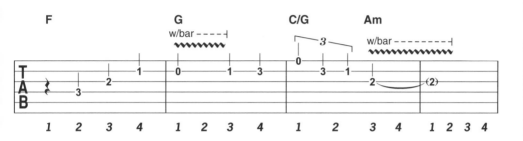

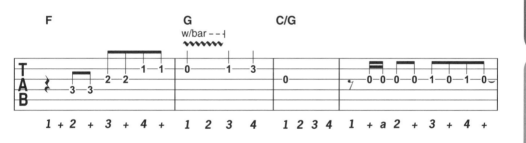

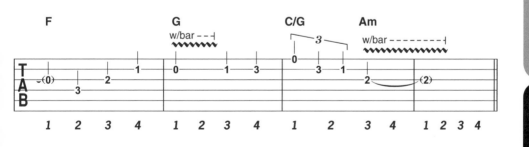

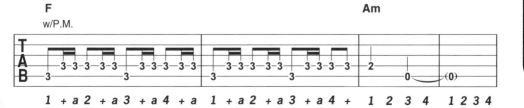

Beginner

Intermediate

Intermediate +

TAB

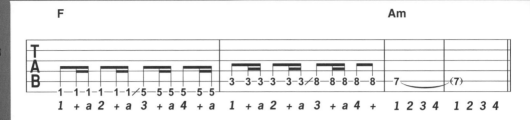

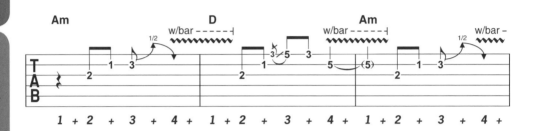

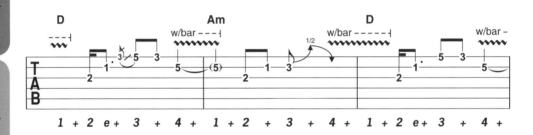

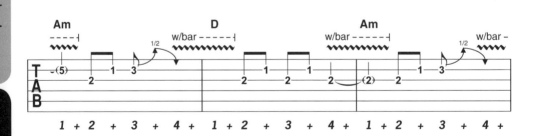

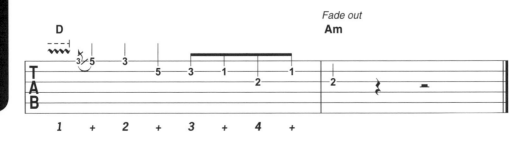

Johnny B. Goode

Words & Music by Chuck Berry

 ## Introduction

Johnny B. Goode is one of the all-time great guitar songs, and one that has had a huge influence on generations of guitar players. If you really dig Chuck Berry then you certainly need to check out T-Bone Walker, whose playing style and stage antics were a huge influence on Chuck Berry.

Listen Up!

Please note before we begin that you must listen to the track—reading the TAB is not enough. There are many things that the page just won't tell you: the time feel, the dynamics, the energy and the vibe. All of these are more fundamental to learning this style than the notes themselves! So listen first.

Please pay specific attention to the loose feel. Even though there is a lot of energy the feel is cool, relaxed and easy, and it needs to feel that way when you play it! This will only come with practice and only really once your technique is above the level that you need to play the song. Working on your picking, left-hand finger independence, bends, and rhythmic accuracy will help you really nail this song. Having the confidence that you can nail it will allow help take the pressure off and allow you to relax into it.

It's interesting to note that the song is played in the key of B♭, which seems a strange one for many guitar players. The reason that quite a few rock 'n' roll songs from the 1950s are in B♭ is because that key is very easy for horn players (trumpet and saxophone) to play in, and often Chuck would have been playing with a pickup band that included these instruments. Many guitar players play it in A which is a more guitar-friendly key, but I'd recommend being brave and playing it in the correct key!

All the while you should be stealing as many licks as you can and learning to use them in other contexts. You can bet your bottom dollar that all the great blues guitar players have been through this song and stolen licks, and there is no shame in it at all—in the blues style you MUST steal licks. Licks are the words that make up the language and being too 'individual' just won't make sense. I'd recommend going through the transcription with a red pen and breaking it down into licks and then trying to re-arrange them in your own improvisations. You'll get a lot from it this way.

Johnny B. Goode

Words & Music by Chuck Berry

Intro

B♭	B♭	B♭	B♭
E♭	E♭	B♭	B♭
F	F	B♭	B♭

Verse 1

      B♭   **B♭**
Deep down in Louisiana, close to New Orleans,

      B♭   **B♭**
Way back up in the woods among the evergreens,

      E♭   **E♭**
There stood a log cabin made of earth and wood

      B♭   **B♭**
Where lived a country boy named Johnny B. Goode,

      F   **F**
Who never ever learned to read or write so well

      B♭   **B♭**
But he could play a guitar just like a-ringing a bell.

Chorus 1

      B♭ **B♭**
Go! Go! Go Johnny, go,

B♭ **B♭**
Go! Go Johnny, go,

E♭ **E♭**
Go! Go Johnny, go,

B♭ **B♭**
Go! Go Johnny, go,

F **F**   **B♭**   **B♭**
Go!   Johnny B. Goode.

Verse 2

He used to carry his guitar in a gunny sack,
Go sit beneath the tree by the railroad track.
Ol' engineer in the train sittin' in the shade,
Strummin' with the rhythm that the drivers made.
The people passin' by, they would stop and stay,
Oh my, but that little country boy could play.

Chorus 2

As Chorus 1

Guitar solo

Chords as Intro

Verse 3

His mother told him, 'Someday you will be a man,
And you will be the leader of a big ol' band.
Many people coming from miles around
To hear you play your music till the sun goes down,
Maybe someday your name'll be in lights
Saying JOHNNY B. GOODE TONIGHT.'

Chorus 3

As Chorus 1 w/ad lib. vocals

Coda

| B♭ | B♭7 |

The Intro

This is easily one of the most recognisable guitar intros of all time—these 12 bars are learned by most guitar players at some point. It's a lot of fun and a great one to have in your repertoire to pull out if you get up and jam with a band. It's got all of Chuck Berry's trademarks: the sliding double stop, the use of the Minor Pentatonic scale, with a few extra notes thrown in (actually it's notes from the Mixolydian mode, but that sounds scary) and the repeating figure of bars 5-8. It's all there in that little intro, so get stuck into it!

Rhythm

It's worth paying some attention to the rhythm guitar when the time comes to learn it. On the original recording it sounds to me like the rhythm guitar is played with all down-picks, which is difficult to maintain for the whole song, but possible with practice. It was almost certainly played in the one position as shown in the tab. However, it was more common in the period to stick to the sixth string root chords and strum all the strings (all but the thickest two being muted). With a little research you will find video evidence of Chuck playing it both ways, so you have some freedom to explore, but I believe that the original recording used down-picks in one position.

You'll find some useful advice on this style of rhythm playing in my Blues Rhythm Guitar Course, available on my website.

Beginner

Intermediate

Intermediate +

TAB

 ## Chorus Licks

Pay attention to the way Chuck Berry uses one lick through the chorus, creating a call and response between the vocals and the guitar. The lick is often changed but the placement and effect it has stays the same.

 ## Solo Rhythm

Make sure you check out the rhythm guitar stops in the solo; these are an important part of the song and if you play the song with a band you will be expected to know these when someone else is taking a solo!

 ## Solo

The solo includes more of Chuck's famous licks over two choruses. You'll start to see similar patterns of notes coming through—these are his favourite licks and to emulate his style it's these that you should pay greatest attention too.

As usual, take it slowly and try your best to get the notes and rhythm right. Having said that, it's worth remembering that this was an improvised solo and some of the notes are less exact in reality than they seem on the page. For example, on beat 4 in the first bar of the solo you see a 6-7 hammer-on, which is correct but you can also hear a hint of string 2 fret 6 in there too, not enough to be written down, but if you play it with the right vibe these little subtleties happen on their own. While accuracy is important, as you get better at playing the solo you can afford to loosen up and let some natural, relaxed 'mistakes' in.

Johnny B. Goode

Words & Music by Chuck Berry

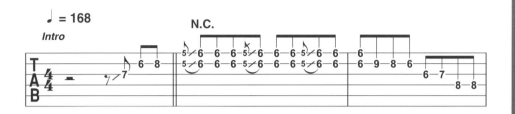

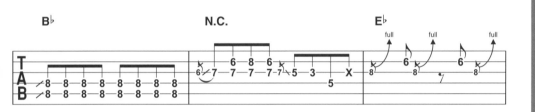

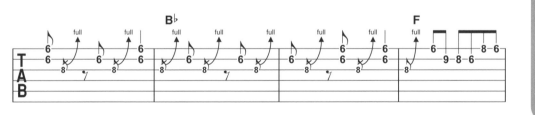

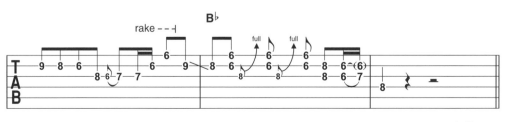

1. Deep

Johnny B. Goode (cont.)

Verse B♭

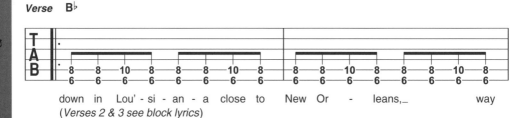

down in Lou' - si - an - a close to   New Or - leans,_   way
(*Verses 2 & 3 see block lyrics*)

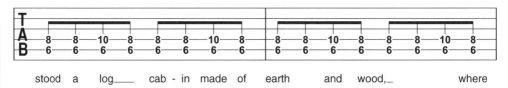

back up   in   the woods a - mong the   e - ver -   greens,   there

E♭

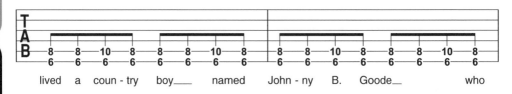

stood a   log____ cab - in made of   earth   and   wood,_   where

B♭

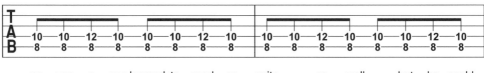

lived   a   coun - try   boy____   named   John - ny   B.   Goode__   who

F

ne - ver   e - ver learned to   read or   write   so   well,__ but   he could

172

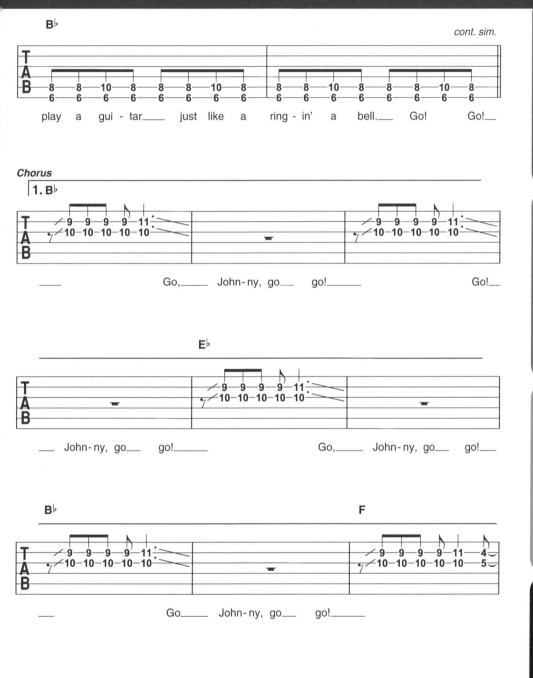

Johnny B. Goode (cont.)

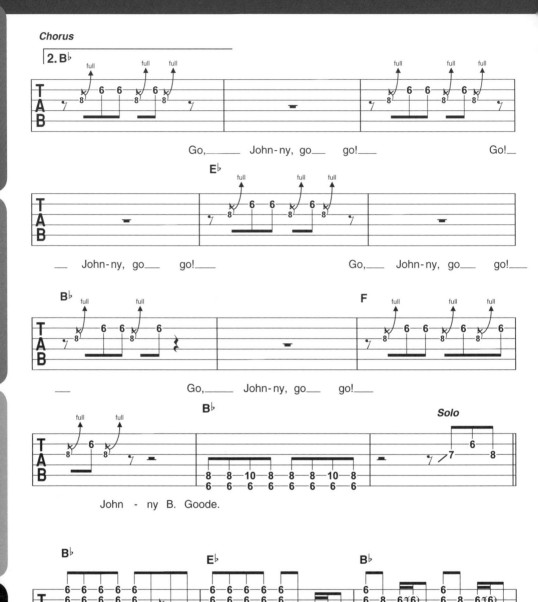

Go,_____ John-ny, go____ go!____ Go!__

__ John-ny, go____ go!____ Go,___ John-ny, go____ go!____

Go,_____ John-ny, go____ go!____

John - ny B. Goode.

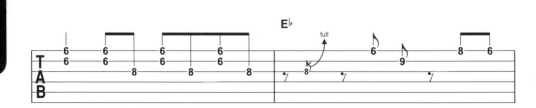

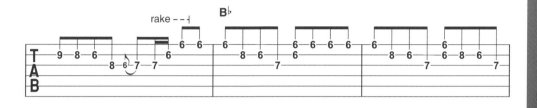

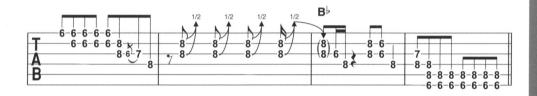

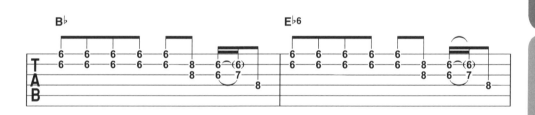

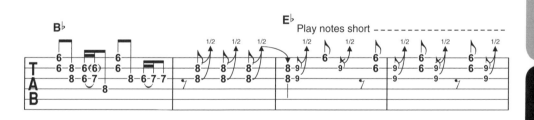

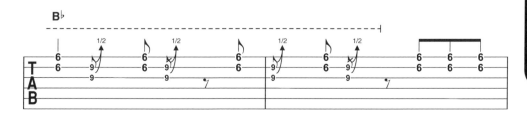

175

Johnny B. Goode (cont.)

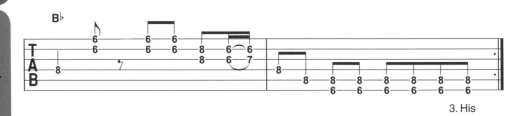

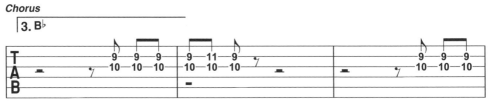

3. His

Chorus

3. B♭

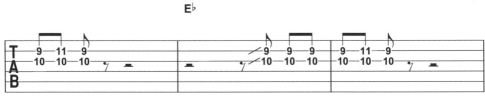

Go_ John - ny, go!_   Go, go, go____ John - ny, go!_

E♭

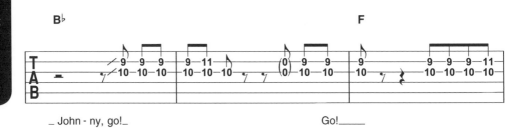

Go, go, go_ John - ny, go!_   Go, go, go_

B♭   **F**

_ John - ny, go!_   Go!____

176

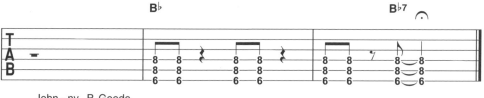

B♭   B♭7

John - ny   B. Goode._____

Verse 2
He used to carry his guitar in a gunny sack
Go sit beneath the tree by the railroad track
Old engineers would see him sittin' in the shade
Strummin' with the rhythm that the drivers made
The people passin' by they would stop and say
'Oh my, but that little country boy could play.'

Verse 3
His mother told him 'Someday you will be a man
And you will be the leader of a big ol' band'
Many people comin' from miles around
Will hear you play your music when the sun go down
Maybe someday your name will be in lights
Sayin', 'Johnny B. Goode tonight'.

177

Hide Away
Words & Music by Freddie King & Sonny Thompson

 ## Introduction

In this tutorial we're going to be looking at Eric Clapton's take on this awesome Freddie King tune. Have a listen to both versions if you like, as they are similar in many ways, although Clapton's cover, recorded in 1966 for John Mayall's *Blues Breakers With Eric Clapton* album, seems a little better known.

 ## Main Melody (A)

The main melody here represents one of the differences between the Eric Clapton / John Mayall recording and the original Freddie King version. Clapton plays the first part of the melody up at the 9th position, while Freddie King plays it in open position. Interestingly it seems that more recently Clapton has played it in open position too, just like Freddie King played it. I would recommend figuring it out in both positions; it's not a hard thing to do by ear, especially as the last part of the melody is shown in open position for you! Make sure you listen closely to the original a few times and cop the groove—as ever, playing along at a slow speed is the best way to nail it.

 ## Solo 1 (B)

The first solo (24 bars) uses a lot of two-note riff ideas, where you let the notes ring together, add in some vibrato and really 'dig in'. There are a lot of triplets too but as is common in the Blues, the written rhythms are approximations—the rhythms that are played are looser and performed in a more relaxed way. Make sure you pay attention to your bends and ensure that they are in tune. To play the 'rake' in Bar 6, fret finger 1 on the note E (string 2, fret 5) and then let fingers 2 and 3 lay down onto the strings above (strings 3 and 4) so that when you strum through strings 4 then 3 they are muted and when you get to string 2 the note will ring out clearly. If this is new to you, it is a technique worth exploring on its own before using in the context of a solo.

178

Unison Riff 1 (C)

The whole band comes together to play this awesome riff. There's nothing too tricky here, especially if you have looked at my 12-Bar Blues Variations lesson in my Beginner's Course, which has a lot in common with this section!

 ## Solo 2 (D)

The second solo starts with 12 bars of classic Minor Pentatonic based licks—they're all really cool to play and are great licks to steal! During the next 12 bars, the band kicks in some rhythmic punctuation while Clapton rips into the chords and then a tricky lick using 6ths which will require a lot of jumping around and plenty of practice to get smooth. Then there are more cool licks to check out—more advanced players should work out the relationships between the notes being played and the chords.

 ## Unison Riff 2 (E)

The energy kicks up a gear for the next unison riff, and the time signature changes as well. The most important thing here is to get the picking right, as for each bar it will be:

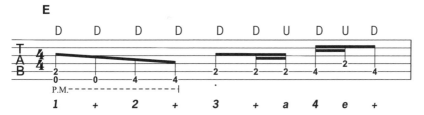

This translates as down-picks on the beats and 'ands' and up-picks on the 'e' and 'a'. Getting the picking right will mean you can really nail the groove, while getting it wrong will result in it never quite feeling right even if you can play the notes!

179

Solo 3 (F)

For the last solo Clapton really starts cooking it, and this section can be tricky to learn as there is a lot going on. The rhythms (back in the 12/8 time signature) are pushing and pulling all over the place but there is so much great stuff going on that I think it's totally worth the effort of learning it.

I always try to break trickier solos down into chunks that I feel I can manage, and then work on the solo one chunk at a time. I'll listen to one section (normally looped using software), playing along at a slower speed to make sure I'm getting it right. Once I feel alright with one bit, I'll move onto the next until I've got the whole thing sounding good enough. Then I'll start playing the whole solo through at a slower speed, between 50% and 70% depending on how confident I feel. If I play it right through I'll begin to speed it up, but if there is one section giving me trouble I'll always stop and work on that one bit until it's at roughly the same level as the rest of the solo. Don't forget that listening is the most effective strategy, because even though you have the TAB to look at, without using your ears you will never get it sounding close to the record, especially with blues music, where there is so much important stuff that just can't be written down!

Hide Away

Words & Music by Freddie King & Sonny Thompson

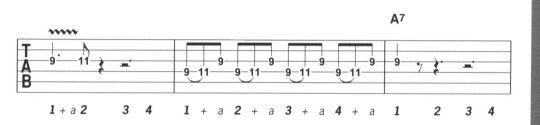

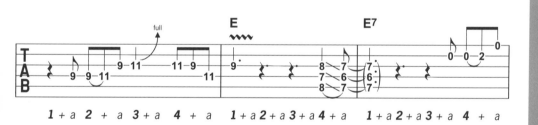

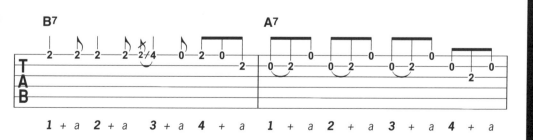

Hide Away (cont.)

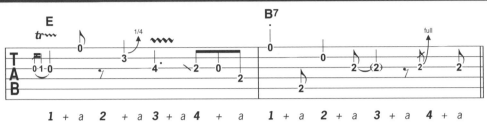

182

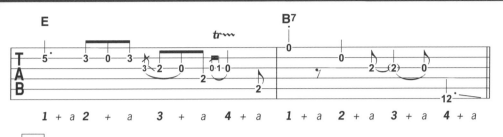

1 + a 2 + a 3 + a 4 + a   1 + a 2 + a 3 + a 4 + a

C

1 + a 2 + a 3 + a 4 + a   1 + a 2 + a 3 + a 4 + a   1 + a 2 + a 3 + a 4 + a

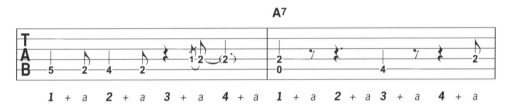

1 + a 2 + a 3 + a 4 + a   1 + a 2 + a 3 + a 4 + a

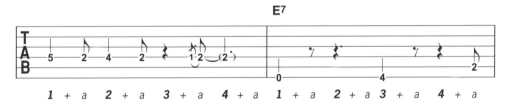

1 + a 2 + a 3 + a 4 + a   1 + a 2 + a 3 + a 4 + a

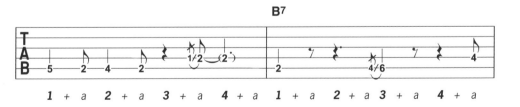

1 + a 2 + a 3 + a 4 + a   1 + a 2 + a 3 + a 4 + a

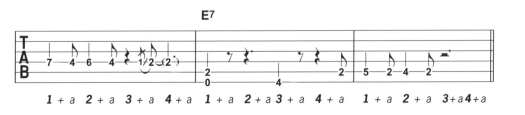

1 + a 2 + a 3 + a 4 + a   1 + a 2 + a 3 + a 4 + a   1 + a 2 + a 3 + a 4 + a

Beginner

Intermediate

Intermediate +

TAB

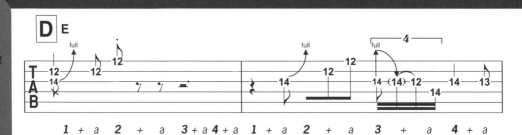

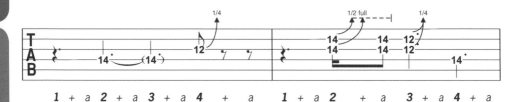

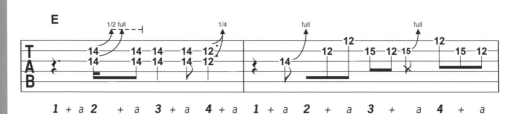

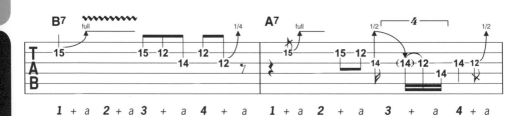

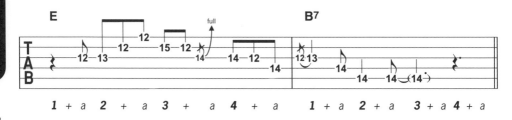

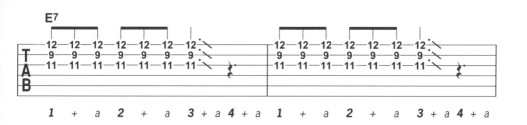

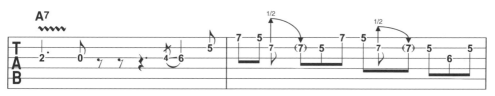

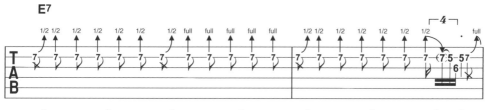

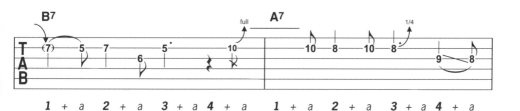

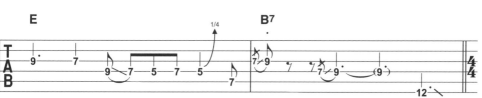

Hide Away (cont.)

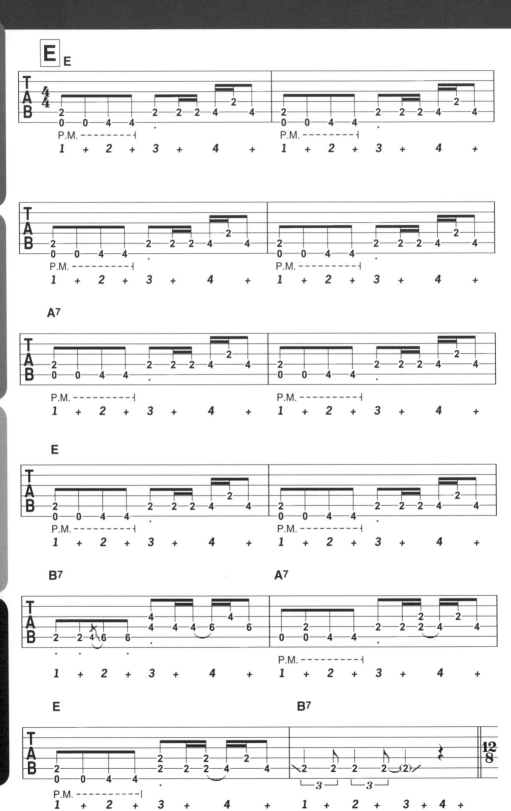

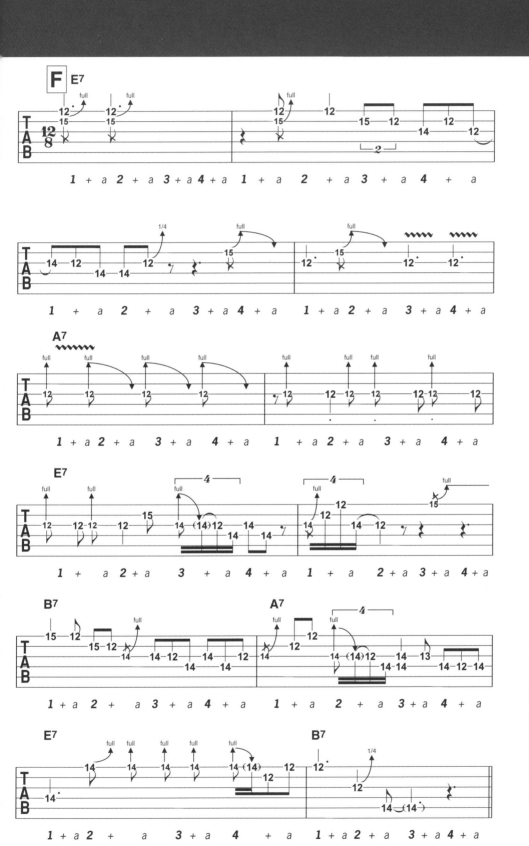

Beginner

Beginner

Intermediate

Intermediate +

TAB

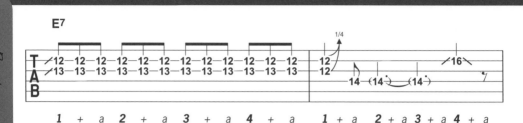

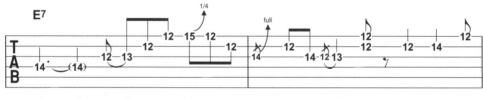

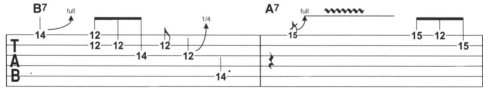

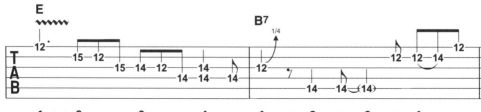

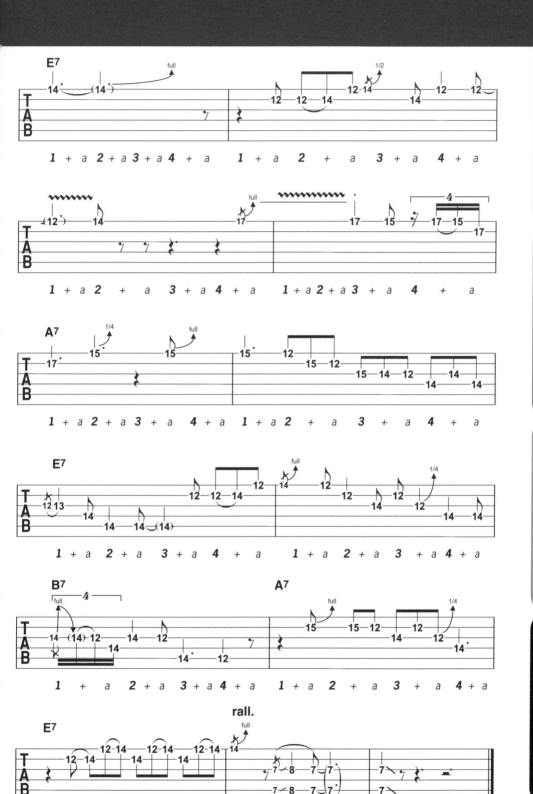

189

Classical Gas
Music by Mason Williams

Beginner
Intermediate
Intermediate +
TAB

 ## Introduction

Mason Williams' 'Classical Gas' is a bone fide guitar masterpiece and was one of the first classical pop crossover hits. I always loved the cover by the great Tommy Emmanuel but the original is the best place to start (and Tommy Emmanuel's version is scarily difficult!).

The recording is played using a nylon string guitar and you'll need to play with your fingers (not a pick) as often two non-adjacent strings are played at one time. An interesting thing for me is that I'd never learned this tune until I decided to put it in the book so I've got fresh experience of learning it to share with you!

 ## Intro (A)

The very beginning of this piece is played quite freely (and labelled 'Recitativo'—meaning 'speech-like'), and so to accurately reproduce it you will need to listen to the original recording. One important thing to understand with this piece (and many others like it) is that you should look for the 'big picture' when it comes to the notes you are playing, because often they are part of a chord. For example, you wouldn't finger the very first two notes individually, as they are simply part of an Am chord. And on beat 1 of bar 3 you will be playing an Em chord even though none of that is shown on the TAB. So how do you know? Well you have to figure it out (usually experience helps) or in this current age you can do a little video research and watch people playing it—in this case you will find some quite good footage of Mason Williams playing it and you'll clearly see him fretting an Em chord and playing the melody line with his little finger!

Note as well that the squiggly arrow is showing that the notes are played slightly separated. Again, it's best to listen to the original recording to get the right feel.

🎵 Main Melody (B)

Now the beat kicks in and you'll need to be accurate with your timing and notes! It's labelled '*più animato*', meaning 'more animated'. Make sure you check out the chord shapes and not just the notes. In the 3rd bar of the melody you'll be playing a full Em chord (using fingers 2 and 3) even though it's not shown on the TAB, and use finger 4 to play the melody line shown. Why? While playing a song like this it's very likely you'll hit these strings by accident, in which case you'll want notes from the right chord to ring out when you do! Also notice that the last note of the 3rd bar (A) will be played as part of the Am shape, which you will change to just before the bar line. This section is repeated.

🎵 Main Melody Ending (C)

Things get a little trickier after the second time through the melody—the trick here is to keep a strong pulse going, using a metronome or tapping your foot. Make sure you have the rhythm internalised, especially when you encounter unusual time signature changes, which we have two of in this little section. Be aware that the whole section uses even eighth-notes except for in the 2/4 bar and the one following it where there a few notes held longer. Remember where these changes occur and then play the rest at a very slow, even tempo and you should have it fairly quickly. Playing slowly is the solution—do it as slowly as you need to get it right!

🎵 The B Section (D)

This part of the melody requires some independence between the thumb and the fingers as you'll want to keep the melody and the bass notes sounding separate. Again, it's all about practising slowly and carefully here because the music becomes a little complex.

Beginner

Intermediate

Intermediate +

TAB

191

The Orchestral Bit (E)

At this point in in the original version, the guitar stops for a while and lets the orchestra take over. Most versions however leave out this section—so just repeat the Dm/A arpeggio a couple of times and crack on with the rest!

 ## Variations / Finger Twisters (F)

The next section contains many variations on themes we have already seen and some completely new material too, much of it quite complex. This section, more than any other, will require slow and careful study. It divides nicely into 2-bar sections so look at each chunk, figure out the fingering and rhythms and play them slowly, over and over until you are happy with them. Then learn the next chunk the same way, and then join it on to the bits you have learned already. If you are uncertain of any part then check the original recording. Those with rhythm reading skills should have fewer problems working out the timings, and if you are struggling you might want to look out for my eBook called Understanding Rhythmic Notation (available on my website) which will teach you the skills needed to interpret rhythmic notation (a valuable skill for those that read tab and not dots!).

NOTE THE D.S. al Coda—this means go to Da Squiggle (𝄋), and then play until the Coda (𝄌). When you reach the coda you jump to the Coda sign, which is the bar after where it tells you to D.S. OK, I confess, D.S actually means Dal Segno which translates as 'to the sign' and the sign is the squiggle!

 ## Outro (G)

The last section (the Coda) is pretty much material you will have seen before with a few minor variations. Take your time through it but most of it should be familiar to you. This section shouldn't take too long to master if you've been meticulous when learning the rest of the song.

I hope you enjoyed learning this all-time, awesome guitar classic!

Classical Gas
Music by Mason Williams

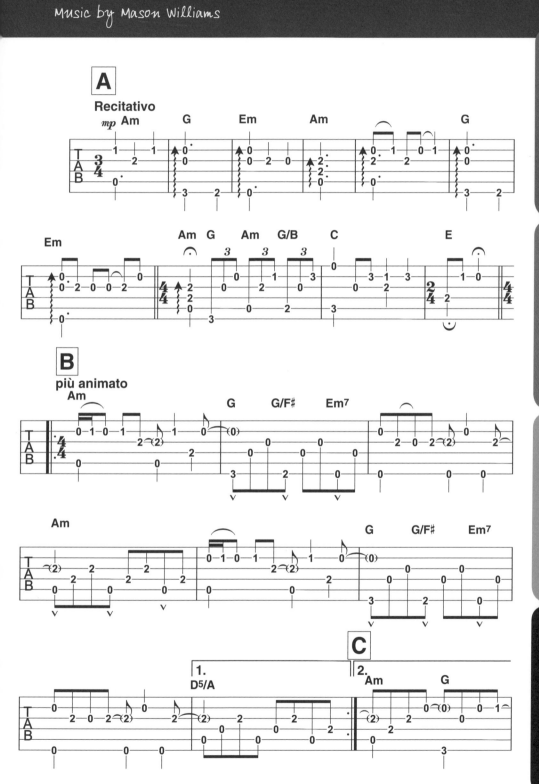

Beginner

Intermediate

Intermediate +

TAB

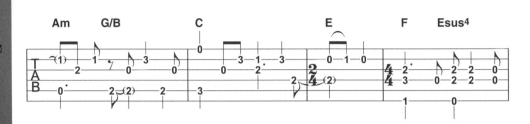

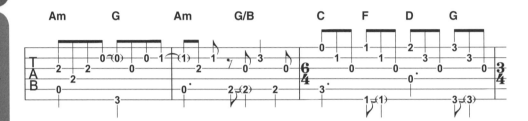

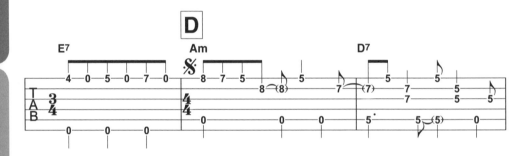

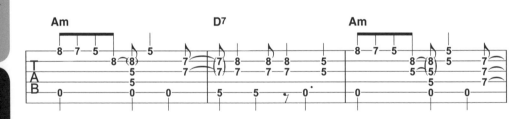

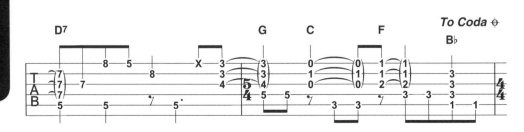

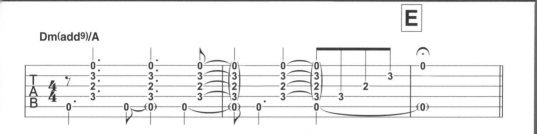

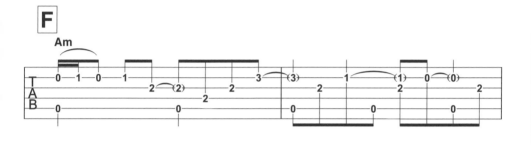

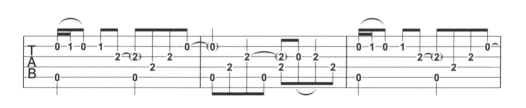

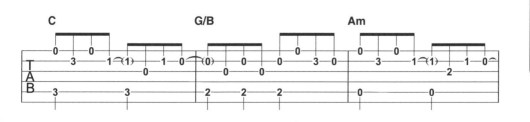

Classical Gas (cont.)

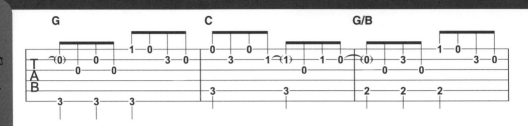

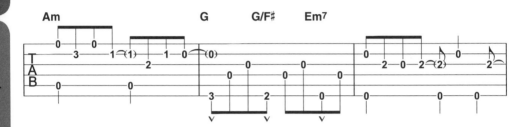

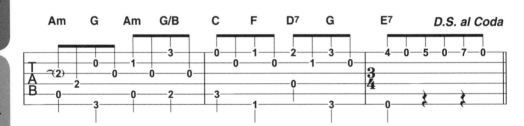

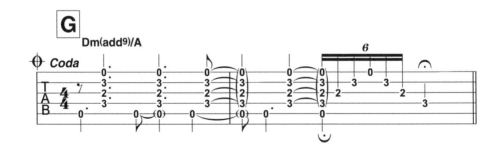

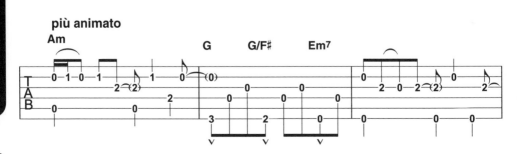

Beginner

Intermediate

Intermediate +

TAB

196

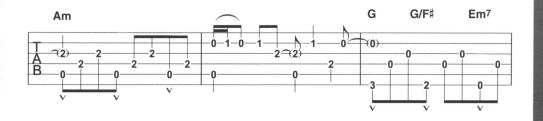

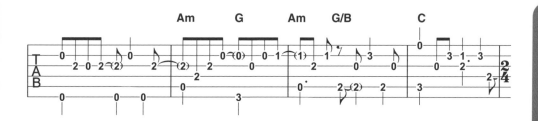

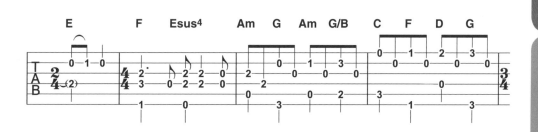

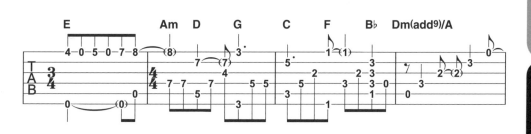

Beginner

Intermediate

Intermediate +

TAB

197

'Cause We've Ended As Lovers
Words & Music by Stevie Wonder

Introduction

In my humble opinion, Jeff Beck is the greatest guitar player that ever lived, and this song is one of his most playable, although it has its fair share of challenges! We'll be focusing on the original version of the song, recorded in 1974 and released on the album *Blow By Blow*.

Before We Begin

Before we start looking at techniques and the specifics of this transcription, it's really important to be aware that Jeff Beck never plays this song the same way twice! In most live versions (you'll find a few on YouTube) he uses the whammy bar a lot but on the original version (on the album *Blow By Blow*—if you don't have it, go get it now!) it's played on a Telecaster fitted with Gibson humbucker pickups—so no whammy bar!

It is important to remember that Jeff Beck plays with his fingers and no pick, although there are times in the original recording where I swear I can hear pick noise (although I guess it must be something else). When you come to play the song, you might like to do it with a pick, or try the fingers version. They sound a little different but neither is inherently 'better' than the other.

Volume Swells (A)

One particular technique that Jeff Beck is a master of is controlling the volume of the guitar. Watch a live video and you'll notice him continually fine-tuning the volume, as it changes the tone, giving him access to a wide variety of tones from just one guitar. At the start of this song (and some other points later on) he uses 'volume swells'. To perform these you should start with your volume completely off, play the note and then fade the volume up. This creates a strange sound, since the original 'attack' of the note has been removed. This technique will take practice and is easier on Stratocaster-type guitars (as the volume knob is much closer to the strings!) but is possible on other guitars too. In this song you will start to release the bent note once the volume is up. To get the note to sustain long enough you most likely need quite a bit of volume, so if you are playing quietly at home, don't be surprised if your notes fade out before you'd like them too. Jeff Beck plays VERY loud.

Beginner

Intermediate

Intermediate +

TAB

Behind The Nut Bend (B)

These days Jeff Beck seems to use the whammy bar to make this little bend but assuming what I have researched is correct and he used a modified Telecaster for the original recording then he must have done this semitone bend by pressing his finger behind the nut. Simply play the open G-string (string 3) and then press behind the nut until you get a semitone lift in pitch. This won't work great on every guitar—I can't get enough bend on my Les Paul, and it won't work at all on a guitar with a locking tremolo system. It's a fun technique and very useful for those of us that play without whammy bars. I believe that Beck dedicated this song to the great Roy Buchanan who was a master of this technique—and check out the awesome Jim Campilongo to hear someone taking it to the next level.

Glissando And Slide (C)

Right through the song Beck uses glissando and slides—sliding a finger up or down a string—but have often chosen not to specify the exact frets to play to and from, and instead have marked them with muted X notes. Seriously, don't worry about getting these slides sounding absolutely identical to the recording, as it probably wasn't very pre-planned when Beck played it—trying to replicate these intricacies accurately is a waste of time and missing the point!

199

Same Note Bend (D)

One of the big debates we had when transcribing this song was about how the bends were performed, particularly as very little video exists from the time of the original recording, and the fact that Beck never plays it exactly the same. To play this lick you'll play the note C (string 1, fret 8, finger 1) and then jump to the note C on the second string (string 2, fret 13, finger 3) to perform a tone-and-a-half bend. You might find this awkward at first but I'm sure this is how it was played on the original recording.

You'll notice just after this lick there is a semitone bend, which will be played with finger 1, which can be very difficult. This kind of awkward bend, especially with finger 1, is a trademark of Beck's style and it will be hard to play this song without working on those techniques.

 ## Accurate Bending (E)

String bending and accuracy in pitch are two of the most important elements when learning a Jeff Beck song. One of his favourite licks is to play a note and then bend up to it from a tone or semitone below, which is what he's doing here. Usually this will require you to bend with finger 1 which is difficult, the other option being to make a very fast 'position jump' which is usually harder and will leave you in an awkward position for the next run. There is no trick, it will just require a lot of practice!

 ## Learning The Flurries? (F)

At certain points in the song you'll hear fast flurries of notes, which are essentially about conveying energy and excitement, and very little to do with the individual notes. Right here is a good example—we slowed down the song and fussed over it to figure out exactly what notes were played, but the end result makes no sense to me when I try and play it! It's just a vibe and if you really want to nail it and want to explore this one bit, then go for it, but I'd recommend working on more important aspects of the song—like performing the melody beautifully—rather than wasting time on an improvised burst of energy that Beck will almost certainly have never played the same again!

How Accurate? (G)

In the next few bars there are some crazy licks and interesting phrases but again, try not to get too caught up in the details. Some of these licks were really played 'in the moment', and trying to reproduce them will be difficult (if not futile) and time-consuming with very little reward. My personal take on learning solos like this is to nail the phrases that make sense to me, and then explore the other phrases for ideas that I can relate to, trying to extract the 'essence' of the phrase and steal it! Five bars after [G] there is a lovely chromatic run which is certainly worth stealing and using in your own improvisations, although some of the other bits in between will be less useful.

 ## Final Thoughts

There is a lot going on in this song, but the most important thing to remember is that it's a beautiful melody! That's the most important thing and you MUST remember not to focus on the fancy stuff until you can really put your heart into that melody and make it sing.

The incredible control that Jeff Beck has over his guitar is something we should all strive for—he truly expresses himself through the instrument and even when he plays the simplest licks they have a noticeable emotional power.

I hope you enjoy playing this song as much as I do—I included the song in this book partly because I'm sure it will be popular with you all, but also because it's been a song I've wanted to learn for a long time but never found the time to examine properly. Having just spent a few hours with it before writing these notes, it was totally worth it, and now that I've got the basics down I need to start the long journey of trying to perfect it.

'Cause We've Ended As Lovers

Words & Music by Stevie Wonder

Beginner

Intermediate

Intermediate +

TAB

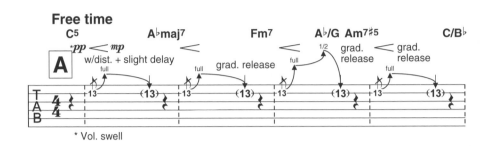

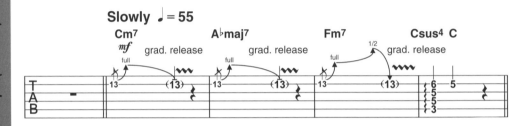

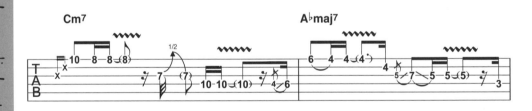

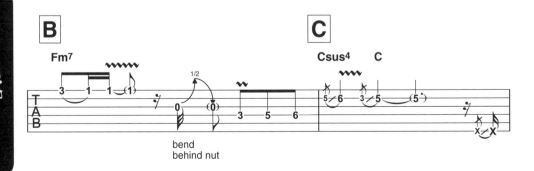

D

Cm⁷

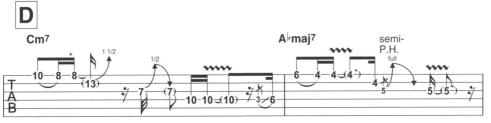

* Played w/ring finger

Fm⁷   Csus⁴ C   D/C   C¹³⁽#⁹⁾

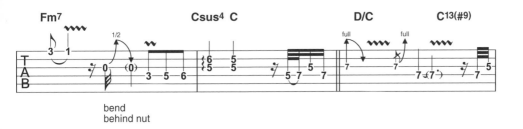

bend
behind nut

Fm⁷   B♭⁷ Fdim/C C   D/C

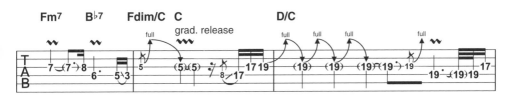

E

Fm⁷   B♭⁷   Csus⁴   C

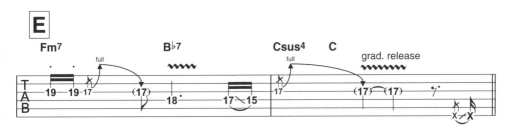

Cm⁷   A♭maj⁷

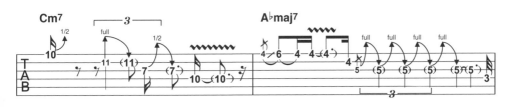

Beginner

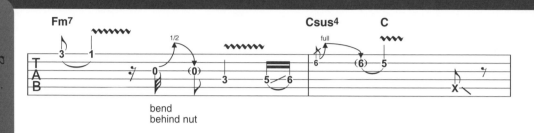

bend
behind nut

Intermediate

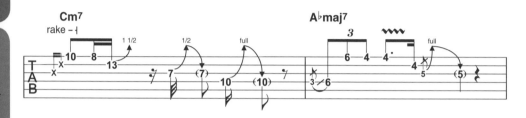

Intermediate

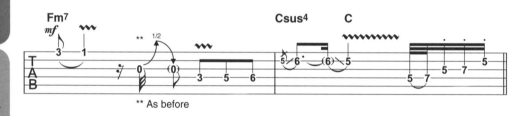

** As before

Intermediate +

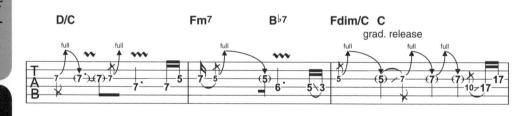

TAB

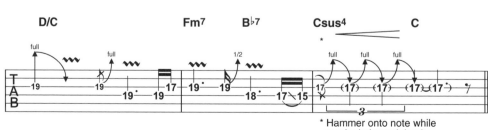

* Hammer onto note while
manipulating vol. knob.

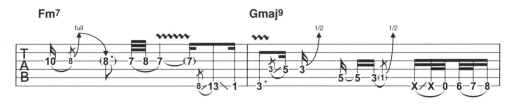

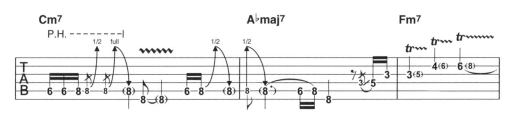

F

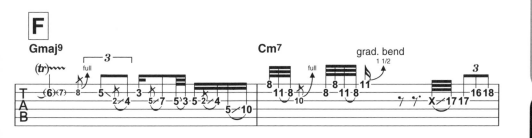

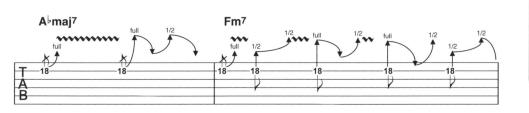

Beginner

Intermediate

Intermediate +

TAB

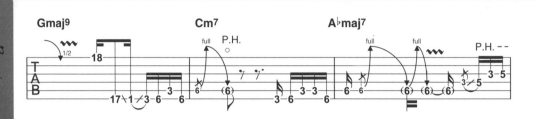

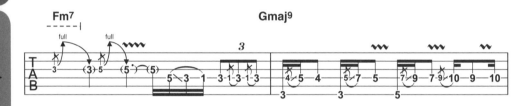

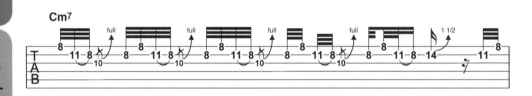

G

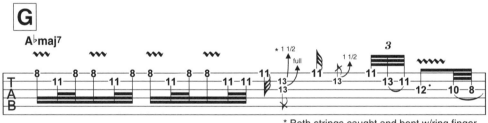

* Both strings caught and bent w/ring finger

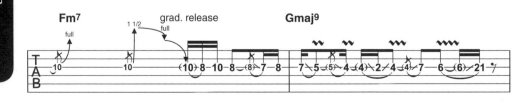

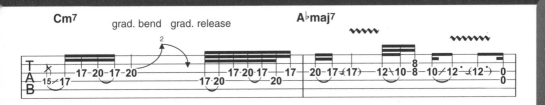

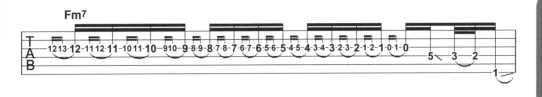

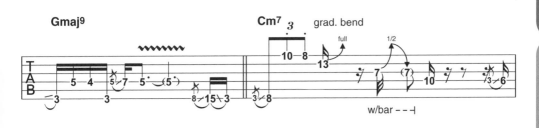

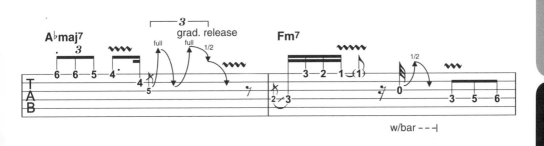

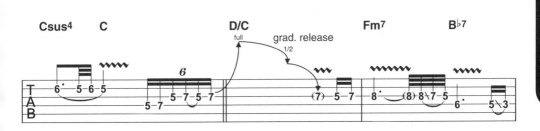

Beginner

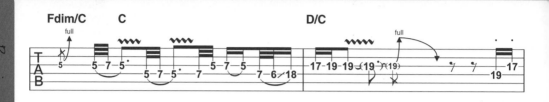

Intermediate

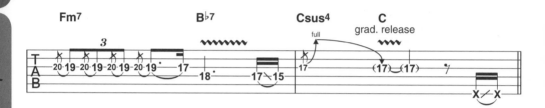

Intermediate +

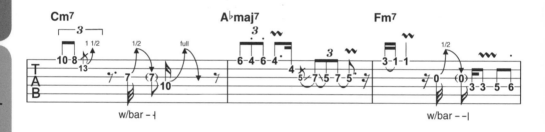

TAB

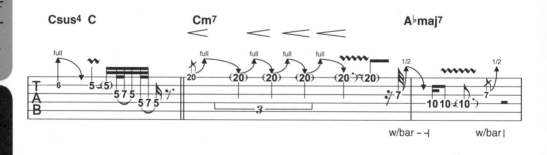

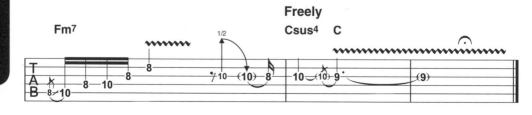